Leeds Art Galleries at Lotherton Hall, Leeds
5 April to 10 June 1979

National Portrait Gallery, London
6 July to 9 September 1979

Detroit Institute of Arts
17 October to 9 December 1979

Cover *Lady Agnew c.1892–3*, detail (no.37)

John Singer Sargent by H. H. Pierce,
Boston, 1924

John Singer Sargent
and the Edwardian age

James Lomax and Richard Ormond

An exhibition organised jointly by the Leeds Art Galleries,
the National Portrait Gallery, London, and the Detroit Institute of Arts

Contents

Exhibition Designers
Christopher Firmstone (London) and Hubert Schmidt (Detroit)

© Leeds Art Galleries and National Portrait Gallery, London, 1979

Published jointly by Leeds Art Galleries, Temple Newsam House, Leeds LS15 0AE,
the National Portrait Gallery, London WC2H 0HE, and the Detroit Institute of Arts,
Detroit, Michigan 48202

Leeds Art Galleries ISBN 0 901981 15 x (paperback)
National Portrait Gallery ISBN 0 904017 26 5 (paperback) 0 904017 27 3 (hardcovers)

Detroit Institute of Arts Library of Congress catalogue card number 79–1755 (paperback)

Catalogue edited by Mary Pettman/National Portrait Gallery

Designed by Graham Johnson/Lund Humphries
Printed in England by Lund Humphries, London and Bradford

Foreword

'The Van Dyck of our times': so Rodin described Sargent. His success with the public was phenomenal. Such bravura and sophistication had not been seen in portraiture in Britain since Lawrence. But bravura is very soon subject to the charge of superficiality; and since his death in 1925 Sargent's reputation has been eclipsed. Moreover, as Richard Ormond writes in his introduction to this catalogue: 'Society portraiture as recent as the Edwardian age still arouses hostility'. Nonetheless, the 'Belle Époque', which was dominated by many of the figures represented in this exhibition, has a particular fascination for us. Was it not an age of unparalleled opulence cataclysmically destroyed by August 1914? And Sargent was its painter *par excellence*. The exhibition devoted mainly to Sargent's more informal work at the Corcoran Gallery of Art in 1964 and the important anthology at Birmingham held in the same year did much to restore his reputation. It is hoped that *John Singer Sargent and the Edwardian age*, the first exhibition to consist exclusively of his portraits and figure sketches, will re-establish him as the distinguished artist he was.

The exhibition evolved in Leeds, London and Detroit. James Lomax, Senior Assistant Keeper at Leeds Art Galleries, originally conceived a show for Lotherton Hall, an Edwardian country house where Sargent's work could be seen in sympathetic surroundings. Richard Ormond, Deputy Director of the National Portrait Gallery, London, who has done fundamental research on the artist in recent years, became closely involved from the outset and Nancy Rivard, Curator of American Art at the Detroit Institute of Arts, who had already begun to plan a Sargent exhibition for the Institute, which houses one of the great collections of American painting, was interested in a joint venture and the exhibition became a major international one. Between them they have chosen the exhibits and James Lomax and Richard Ormond have compiled the catalogue. An exhibition on this scale could not take place without the hard work and organisational abilities of many of our museum colleagues and here we pay particular tribute to Kathleen Pyne, Assistant Curator of American Art, and Susan Weinberg, Registrar, in Detroit, Jacquie Meredith, Exhibitions Officer of the National Portrait Gallery in London, and Peter Walton, Keeper of Lotherton Hall, in Leeds.

The exhibition could not have been shown in Leeds without the generous assistance of the Arts Council of Great Britain, the English Tourist Board, the Yorkshire and Humberside Tourist Board and the help of two Yorkshire-based companies, the Leeds and Bradford Boiler Company and George E. Lowe Ltd. The Detroit showing was made possible with the aid of a grant from the National Endowment for the Arts.

Her Majesty The Queen and Her Majesty Queen Elizabeth The Queen Mother have graciously lent works to the exhibition, and we wish to express our warmest gratitude to them and to the many museums and private lenders who have been so forbearing over our requests for loans. Particular thanks are due to the Ormond family, whose wholehearted co-operation has been invaluable.

Robert Rowe
Director, Leeds Art Galleries

John Hayes
Director, National Portrait Gallery

Frederick Cummings
Director, Detroit Institute of Arts

List of lenders

Her Majesty Queen Elizabeth II 66

Her Majesty Queen Elizabeth the Queen Mother 77

Aberdeen Art Gallery and Museums 8, 87 98

Albright-Knox Art Gallery, Buffalo 9

Mr and Mrs Paul Amir 38

The Visitors of the Ashmolean Museum, Oxford 33

Lady Anne Bentinck 48

Birmingham City Museums and Art Gallery 65

Museum of Fine Arts, Boston 10, 91, 95

The Trustees of the British Museum 14, 56

The Brooklyn Museum 31

Brotherton Library, University of Leeds 26

Carlton Club, London 51

Robert A. Cecil 57

The Trustees of the Chatsworth Settlement 47

Art Institute of Chicago 42

Lady Diana Cooper 72

Corcoran Gallery of Art, Washington DC 12

The Rt Hon The Earl of Dalhousie, KT 44

J. M. de Navarro 69

Detroit Institute of Arts 18

The Syndics of the Fitzwilliam Museum, Cambridge 29, 55, 75

Flint Institute of Arts, Michigan 21

Mrs Alice Gwynne 78

Ben Harrison 84

Miss Philippa Harrison 27

Ian Hugo Hughes 34, 36

The Trustees of the Imperial War Museum 100, 101

Helen Foresman Spencer Museum of Art, University of Kansas 11

W. John Koch 70

Musée du Louvre 35

Dr and Mrs John J. McDonough 22

Simon McInnes 74

Metropolitan Museum of Art, New York 13

Sir Anthony Meyer, Bt 41

National Galleries of Scotland 37

National Museum of Wales, Cardiff 102

National Portrait Gallery, London 39, 49, 52, 53, 58, 59

National Trust (Chartwell) 79

Nigel Nicolson 60

Mrs Edward Norman-Butler 71

The Ormond Family 2, 3, 6, 7, 15, 17, 19, 23, 24, 25, 32, 40, 67, 88, 92, 93, 96, 97

David Tree Parsons 63

Denys Parsons 64

The late Lady Richmond 80, 83

Royal Academy of Arts, London 94

Sir Charles Russell, Bt 45

Fine Arts Museum of San Francisco 20

Mrs Antony Sefi 73

Sheffield City Art Galleries 16

Sheila Sonne 50

Southampton Art Gallery 28

Major-General John Swinton, OBE 62

Tate Gallery, 30, 46

Musée National, Versailles 5

Victoria and Albert Museum 89

The Earl of Wemyss and March, KT 76

York City Art Gallery 61

Lent anonymously 1, 4, 43, 54, 68, 81, 82, 85, 86, 90, 99

Acknowledgements

We are enormously grateful for the generosity, hospitality and encouragement of the large number of people who have shown their enthusiasm in the preparation of this exhibition. Sargent's descendants, the Ormond family, have given us their unstinting support, as have all the private lenders represented here, and many others. Amongst these we are particularly grateful to Nigel Nicolson, and to Major-General and Mrs John Swinton for bringing new information to our attention. Our enquiries at collections in Great Britain and the United States and on the Continent were patiently dealt with by Captain Alistair Aird, Hugh Bett, Peter Day, Rosemary Gilbert, Anne Goodchild, Linn Hardenburgh, Janet Hughes, David Masson, Milo M. Naeve, the Hon Mrs John Roberts, Theodore Stebbins, Derrick Worsdale and Christopher Young. Our special thanks are due to John Sunderland and the staff of the Witt Library.

Mary Pettman undertook the task of editing the catalogue and seeing it through the press with admirable efficiency. We are sincerely grateful to her and to all our colleagues, particularly Terry Friedman, Jill Gerrish, Miranda Strickland-Constable and Heather Tilbury for their advice and suggestions. Finally, we must thank Graham Johnson and Lund Humphries for designing and producing another of their splendid catalogues.

James Lomax
Richard Ormond

Introduction

Fig.1 With Monet (behind left), and Paul and Alice Helleu at the Exposition Universelle, Paris, 1889. By courtesy of Mrs P. Howard-Johnston

Society portraiture as recent as that of the Edwardian age still arouses hostility. Sargent's portraits are too often seen in terms of aesthetic and social preconceptions. We are still dogged by the repercussions of the modernist debate with its labels and categories. A portraitist in the grand manner is *per se* suspect as an artist, whatever the quality of his work.

Ultimately, like all great portrait painters, Sargent succeeds in so far as he moves us. In his best work it is impossible to separate the intensity of life and personality that he communicates from the bravura means used to achieve it. That his colour and brushwork are frankly enjoyable is not in itself a symptom of superficiality. As D. S. MacColl recognized in *Ena and Betty* (no.46) design only came to Sargent when he was excited, 'a design discovered in the material, and sway of one figure to the other, and the run of light along the turned out arm and downstroke of the fan'.

Sargent's formal portraits record the social type no less than the individual, the values of an opulent and self-confident age. His painterly energy and largeness of spirit were matched to sitters who commanded beauty, wealth and authority. He conjured them up in designs of great splendour and vitality that set them before us as living characters in spaces that breathe with light and atmosphere. Of course his sitters are larger than life. But formal portraiture has always been concerned with the ennoblement and enhancement of human character. The service rendered by Van Dyck to the Caroline court, Sargent performed for the Edwardian aristocracy and *nouveaux riches*. That his greatest patron was a Bond Street art dealer and not a duke is a comment on the nature of Edwardian society. He painted Asher Wertheimer and his family for what they were, with sympathy but without flattery, in a series of imposing, and sometimes penetrating works.

Sargent's portraits of the Edwardians, the product of his London years, are the centre-piece of the exhibition and its chief *raison d'être*. Ultimately Sargent's reputation rests on his achievement as a portraitist, for, though his landscapes and figure studies can be dazzling, they are a less distinctively original contribution. On the other hand, to think of Sargent solely as a portrait painter, and a fashionable one at that, is to underestimate his range and the length of his career.

The early portraits painted in Paris will surely give the lie to the frequently expressed view that Sargent lacked psychological insight. Here, in designs of great elegance and subtlety, painted it is true with a telling eye for the values of light and dark but in a restrained, taut style, he hints at the complexities of human personality. His sitters emerge from dimly lit backgrounds alert with nervous sensitivity. His groups like the *Boit Children* (no.10) and the *Misses Vickers* (no.16) abound with psychological nuances and dissonances, underscored by his use of asymetrical composition, and his feeling for the mysteriousness of light in shadowed spaces. In the Paris of the early eighties Sargent seems to have absorbed many influences apart from the purely artistic, which have been little explored or understood. His circle of friends included several notable writers, aesthetes and decadents like Paul Bourget and Robert de Montesquiou, and his own reading was voracious and

Colour plate I
Edouard Pailleron 1879 (no.5)

Colour plate II
Mrs Henry White 1883 (no.12)

Colour plate III
Madame Paul Poirson 1885 (no.18)

Colour plate IV
In a Garden c.1883–5 (no.19)

Fig.2 In his studio at 31 Tite Street, c.1900. *Madame X* (no.13) is visible behind

Fig.3 From left to right: Baron Louis von Solberstein, Asher Wertheimer, Antonio Mancini, Sargent and Edward Wertheimer, at Temple near Henley. By courtesy of the Mathias Family

unusual; he died reading Voltaire, and a study of his large library would reveal some unexpected tastes. He was also a passionate music lover and an accomplished pianist. Because as an older man he was so averse to expressing his feelings, so blunt and brusque in his speech, he was often assumed to be simpler and more straightforward than he really was. And the young Sargent, caught up in the febrile world of literary and artistic Paris, was a very different creature from the habitué of polite London drawing-rooms. Meeting him in 1881, after an interval of some years, Vernon Lee described the impression he made on her (*Letters*, 1937, p.63):

John is extremely serious, a great maker of theories; he goes in for art for art's sake, says that the subject of a picture is something not always in the way, etc. He is quite emancipated from all religious ideas. He speaks English without accent, but has to help himself out with French words.

Later, in her 'Memorial Essay', she wrote perceptively of his liking for the strange and exotic (Charteris 1927, pp.252–3):

It may also have been connected with the Parnassian, the Heredia and Lecomte de Lisle movement in literature. I can conceive that at any other time than the eighties or nineties, and with any other surroundings than the expensive and traditionless 'Tastefulness' of the worldly people who sat for him this *bizarre* element might have vanished from Sargent's work.

The 'bizarre element' persists throughout Sargent's work, emerging not only in its more extravagant forms, as in the studies of Javanese dancers or of his nieces in Turkish costume, but also in his choice of accessories for portraits, the placing of an arm or the abrupt foreshortening of a figure. In his mature work Sargent never divorced the principle of design from his practice of realizing a spontaneous impression of his sitter as seen in front of him on the sitter's stand. But his power of design, which seems so instinctive by the nineties, was forged in the much more deliberately constructed and stylized portraits of his French period. His impressionistic technique would have been useless without his ability to compose fluently on a grand scale. And that ability enabled Sargent constantly to enrich his style by absorbing influences from the portraitists of the past, Velazquez, Hals, Van Dyck, Reynolds and Ingres.

But what of Sargent's technique, which, in the eyes of many people, is his chief gift; his unerring eye and sheer brilliance of touch? It was in the atelier of Carolus-Duran, one of the most advanced in Paris, that Sargent learnt this facility with the brush, the ability to paint objects accurately in terms of their light and dark values, and thereby to achieve astonishingly realistic effects. Velazquez was all the rage in the studios of Paris, and Sargent described himself to Vernon Lee as 'an impressionist and an "intransigeant", entirely given up to the faithful reproduction of "les valeurs".' There was no effect of light on form that Sargent could not immediately record on canvas in a few swift strokes. Carolus-Duran's insistence that his students should learn from the beginning to paint *au premier coup* (touch by touch without reworking) explains Sargent's amazing technical accomplishment.

Very early on in his Paris career Sargent fell under the sway of the impressionists, like many other aspiring young painters of his generation. Carolus-Duran himself was a friend of Manet, and linked to the progressive tendencies

Fig.4 Painting out-of-doors, perhaps at Calcot or Fladbury, c.1888–9

Fig.5 The studio at 31 Tite Street, c.1920

Fig.6 Painting *The Brook* (no.88), Purtud, Val d'Aosta, 1907

in contemporary French art. A handful of outdoor studies by Sargent, dating from the late seventies, show him adopting an impressionist technique and palette. During the early eighties he was preoccupied by portraiture, and his subject pictures, like the Spanish and Venetian scenes, are mostly tonal exercises painted indoors. But around 1883 Sargent once more turned to landscape, and during the next six years painted a series of brilliant impressionist scenes where the influence of Monet is paramount. The effect on his portraiture was profound. The freedom of brushwork that one associates with his portraits of the nineties, their scintillating effects of light, warm colour and radiant feeling of space, were the fruits of that experimental phase.

The influence of the impressionists on Sargent's style is self-evident, but it is not easy to document. The date of his first meeting with Monet, who became a close friend, is not certain, the chronology of his visits to Giverny (Monet's house) vague, and the quality of their relationship difficult to assess. Of Sargent's links with other impressionists even less is known. The disparaging comments about him by Degas and Pissarro belong to a later period when he was already successful. Mary Cassatt is known to have liked and admired him as a younger man (and he helped her to secure commissions), and Berthe Morisot attempted to enlist him as a contributor to a planned impressionist exhibition in 1883. He did show with them the following year in an exhibition organized by the radical group, Les XX, in Brussels. With Monet, Sargent led the campaign to buy Manet's *Olympia* for the Louvre as a memorial to him, but again there is a tantalizing lack of evidence about this particular friendship. Until the broader history of impressionism comes to be written, the relationship of artists like Sargent to the main movement will remain unclear.

Though the English critics and public were initially hostile to Sargent's impressionistic style, the tide was running in his favour. The founding of the New English Art Club in 1886 demonstrated the direction which many younger artists were taking, inspired by developments in Paris. By the early nineties Sargent was recognized as a major force. His influence on imitators continued to be deplored, but no one could accuse *him* of ugly or slapdash work. His portraits stood out on the walls of the Academy with electrifying force, killing everything near them. Sargent became much sought after, and the burden of portrait commissions, coupled with the murals he had agreed to paint for the Boston Public Library, occupied his time to the exclusion of everything else. He was caught up in the toils of society, a large man of few words but strong opinions, not much given to showing his feelings but devoted to his family and circle of intimate friends; a personality on the grand scale, who would rush at his canvas from a long distance muttering strange oaths and imprecations to dash in a stroke before retiring to view the result.

During the nineties Sargent painted on average ten or twelve portraits a year, during the early 1900s as many as twenty or twenty-five. Their quality is variable, for there were many sitters who raised no particular spark of sympathy or excitement in him. But the examples shown in this exhibition are of high quality, and they are representative of the range and strength of his powers.

Fig.7 Playing chess with Wilfrid de Glehn (right), Purtud(?), c.1907

Fig.8 Painting at the Simplon Pass, Switzerland, c.1911

In his large portraits Sargent conforms to the age-old conventions of formal portraiture. His women are brilliant creatures of fashion, his poets visionaries, his statesmen statesmanlike. No one would mistake Swettenham (no.49) for anything but an imperial proconsul. The Duchess of Portland (no.48) has all the dignified beauty and nervous refinement of the highly-bred. Social caste and type are implicit in all Sargent's portraits. But his approach to his sitters is rarely stereotyped. He sees them from unexpected angles, in odd juxtapositions with props, or simply projected against suggestive spaces. Light, observed under the conditions of a particular moment, plays across his canvases and envelops his sitters. The surface texture of his work is often scintillating; there are all kinds of felicities of handling and colour, but everything in his art is subservient to the realization of a single coherent impression. His sitters are caught in the midst of active life, posed for an instant before they turn and move, compelling because they are so real. Sargent can suggest the nervous forces and tensions below the surface in the turn of a head, the attitude of a hand, no less than in his capturing of transient expression. His bravura style was a means of realizing the truth about his sitters, not an end in itself.

Sargent's career as a portraitist began to run down around 1907–8. He had achieved all that he needed in the way of worldly success, and he wanted more freedom to pursue his experiments in landscape and mural art. He was not able entirely to escape from his reputation, as the large number of surviving charcoal portraits testifies. They were dashed off in sittings of an hour or two, with the same economy of means and vitality as the oil portraits. No country house seems complete without its Sargent drawing propped up on a table or an easel. Sargent's qualities as a draughtsman have received less than their fair due. The best of his charcoals show how his vivid perception of character can transcend the limitations of a particular medium and style.

The theme of this exhibition, which is devoted to portraits and figure studies, has necessarily limited the type of informal study and landscape that could be included. From 1900 onwards the number of landscapes in oil and water-colour that Sargent painted on his annual holidays in Europe was prodigious. That insatiable curiosity and appetite for painting was now expended on scenes in Italy, Spain and the Alps. In densely impasted oils and broadly washed water-colours his style achieves a new richness and freedom of expression. Here is Adrian Stokes describing him at work on a water-colour of Alpine rocks:

His hand seemed to move with the same agility as when playing over the keys of a piano. That is a minor matter; what was really marvellous was the rightness of every touch . . . All was rendered, or suggested, with the utmost fidelity. Parts were loaded, parts were painted clear and smooth, every touch was individual and conveyed a quick unerring message from the brain. It was, if you will, a kind of shorthand, but it was magical!

The pleasure that a Sargent landscape gives is immediate and instinctive. One responds to the truth of impression – the evocation of form through light, the vibrancy of colour, the force of the brushstrokes themselves. Always the essence of the subject is given, however varied the forms or the light effects. He never paints a set scene. He prefers close-ups, aspects of a building or landscape that suddenly catch his imagination. Sometimes his involvement

Fig.9 With Sir Philip Sassoon (left), and Lord and Lady Rocksavage, c.1920

with a particular motif is so direct that the surface of his picture takes on a life and energy of its own.

Sargent was not, however, merely a painting machine. His intelligence as an artist is revealed not only in the way he composes a picture but in his predilection for certain types of subject. There is an element of fantasy and romance in the pictures of his nieces and their friends in Turkish dress painted beside the brook at Purtud (nos. 88 and 89). These odalisques merge with their surroundings in bold and luxuriant designs. The Cashmere shawl, with its sinuous folds and elegant textures, was the motif of another series of consciously decorative pictures. And these in turn were succeeded by paintings and water-colours of girls reclining in Alpine meadows with ballooning dresses and parasols. These pictures of beautiful and passive girls are mood pieces, but Sargent can also convey character when he chooses. The picture of his sister Emily and Miss Wedgwood reading under mosquito nets (no.92) reveals much about these cultivated middle-aged ladies. And the water-colour of a Spanish wineshop (no.82) is a marvellous essay in atmosphere and character, painted with effortless ease.

Sargent's sketching holidays in Europe ceased with the outbreak of war in 1914; Sargent himself was trapped for some weeks in the Austrian Tyrol. His later landscapes and figure works, painted in the Rockies (1916), Florida (1917), as a war artist in France (1918), and later in New England, are concerned with new themes. The stimulus of Alpine scenery, and the *dolce far niente* mood inspired by his nieces, was gone for ever. Sargent's last years were dominated by mural work for the Boston Museum of Fine Arts as well as the Library, and by commissions for two major war pictures, *Gassed* (Imperial War Museum, London), and *Some General Officers of the Great War* (National Portrait Gallery, London). His death from heart failure in 1925 at the age of sixty-nine was quite unexpected. Obituaries acclaimed him as the greatest portraitist of his generation, and there were major retrospective exhibitions in Boston, New York and London, the last including over five hundred works. The studio sale at Christie's in 1925 fetched over £180,000, a huge sum for those days. Since then his reputation has been eclipsed, but it is hoped that the present exhibition may help to rehabilitate him as a major artist.

Richard Ormond

Fig.10 At the Simplon Kulm Hotel, Switzerland, 1909. From left to right: Sargent, Mrs Barnard, Polly Barnard, Dorothy Barnard, Emily Sargent, the daughters of Signor Tommasini (an Italian friend), Tommasini's wife, unknown and Tommasini

Fig.11 With Colonel Livermore, Rockies, 1916

Chronology

1856   17 January. Sargent born in Florence.

1874   May. Entered the studio of Carolus-Duran.
        October. Began studies at the École des Beaux Arts.

1877   First exhibited at the Salon: portrait of *Miss Watts*.

1878   *Oyster Gatherers of Cancale* exhibited at the Salon: gained second-class medal. Summer and autumn on Capri.

1879   *Carolus-Duran* exhibited at the Salon. Began his professional career. Winter and New Year in southern Spain and Morocco.

1880   Visited Haarlem to study Frans Hals. Summer and autumn in Venice.

1881   In London.

1882   First exhibited in London: at the Royal Academy (portrait of *Doctor Pozzi*), the Fine Art Society, and the Grosvenor Gallery.

1884   *Madame X* exhibited at the Salon. Summer and autumn in England.

1885–6 Moved to England. Summers at Broadway. First exhibited at the New English Art Club.

1887   *Carnation, Lily, Lily, Rose* exhibited at the Royal Academy. Purchased by the Chantrey Bequest. Autumn in USA.

1888   First exhibited at the New Gallery.

1889   Father died.

1890   USA. Many portraits. Received commission to decorate Boston Library.

1891   *La Carmencita* exhibited at the Royal Academy. Purchased by the Musée du Luxembourg.

1894   Elected Associate of the Royal Academy.

1897   Elected full Academician.

1898   Began series of portraits of the Wertheimer family.

1904   First exhibited at the Royal Society of Painters in Water-Colours.

1905   Mother died. Thereafter spent most summers on the Continent with friends and relatives.

1907   First exhibited at the Pastel Society.

1910   Sargent's portraits at the Royal Academy began to be superseded by landscapes.

1914   In Austrian Tyrol at the outbreak of war.

1916   USA. Completed Boston Library decorations. Received commission to decorate Boston Museum of Fine Arts.

1918   In France as official war artist.

1925   15 April. Died in Tite Street, Chelsea.

Abbreviations

Birmingham 1964 — *Exhibition of Works by John Singer Sargent*, City Museum and Art Gallery, Birmingham, 1964

Boston 1925 — *Memorial Exhibition of the Works of the late John Singer Sargent*, Museum of Fine Arts, Boston, 1925

Boston 1956 — *Sargent's Boston*, Museum of Fine Arts, Boston, 1956 (exhibition catalogue, with check-list of all Sargent's portraits, for references to which see Mckibbin)

Charteris 1927 — Hon Evan Charteris, *John Sargent*, London and New York, 1927

Downes 1925 — W. H. Downes, *John S. Sargent: his Life and Work*, Boston, 1925; London, 1926

Falmouth 1962 — *John Singer Sargent*, Polytechnic, Falmouth, 1962

London 1926 — *Exhibition of Works by the late John S. Sargent, R.A.*, winter exhibition, Royal Academy of Arts, London, 1926

Mckibbin 1956 — David Mckibbin, *Sargent's Boston*, Museum of Fine Arts, Boston, 1956 (check-list of portraits)

Meynell 1903, 1927 — *The Work of John S. Sargent, R.A.*, with an introductory note by Mrs Meynell, London and New York, 1903; revised and enlarged edition, with introductions by J. B. Manson and Mrs Meynell, London and New York, 1927

Mount 1955, 1969 — Charles Merrill Mount, *John Singer Sargent: a Biography*, New York, 1955; abridged edition, London, 1957; Kraus reprint of 1955 edition (with updated catalogue), New York, 1969

Mount, *Art Quarterly*, 1963 — C. M. Mount, 'Carolus-Duran and the Development of Sargent', *Art Quarterly*, XXVI, Detroit, 1963, pp.385–417

New York 1926 — *Memorial Exhibition of the Work of John Singer Sargent*, Metropolitan Museum of Art, New York, 1926

Ormond 1970 — Richard Ormond, *John Singer Sargent*, London and New York, 1970

Paris 1963 — *John S. Sargent*, Centre Culturel Americain, Paris, 1963

R.A. — Royal Academy

Tate Gallery 1926 — *National Gallery, Millbank [now Tate Gallery]. List of Loans at the Opening Exhibition of the Sargent Gallery*, 1926

Washington 1964 — *The Private World of John Singer Sargent*, Corcoran Gallery of Art, Washington, and elsewhere, 1964–5

Colour plate V
Mrs Robert Harrison 1886 (no.27)

Colour plate VI
Coventry Patmore 1894 (no.39)

Catalogue

Catalogue entries are arranged chronologically within each section.

Measurements are given in centimetres and (in brackets) inches, height before width.

Reference photographs of Sargent and his friends are reproduced by courtesy of the Ormond family, except where otherwise stated.

Paris

Sargent received a somewhat haphazard education by modern standards. The family travelled continually throughout Europe, but this was an inducement to his intellectual development rather than the reverse, and he became fluent in French and Italian and showed considerable ability in German. He was an excellent pianist, and, not unusually among Victorians, his curriculum included draughtsmanship. From an early age he showed an extraordinary skill at topographical drawings and portraits and this was encouraged by his mother and their large circle of friends. Although his father wished him to join the Navy, Sargent's career as an artist was settled by 1868, and during the winters of the early 1870s he attended classes at the highly unsatisfactory Accademia delle Belle Arti in Florence.

By 1874 it had become clear that Sargent should have the best possible training, and the choice of apprenticeship lay between London and Paris. It seems extraordinary how vague the family were on the implications behind this important decision. In April 1874 Sargent wrote to a cousin from Florence: 'The Academy in Paris is probably better than the one here and we hear that the French artists, undoubtedly the best now-a-days, are willing to take pupils in their studios.' The family moved to Paris with the all-important question as to which studio Sargent should join still in the air and it was only the fortuitous meeting of an old friend in the Boulevard that resolved the issue. Sargent wrote to a friend on 23 May: 'An artistic friend with whom I had sketched last winter in Florence and whom I met a day or two ago, gave me the most particular information I have yet received on the subject. He told me that he was himself in the atelier of M. Carolus-Duran whom he prefers to any other artist in Paris, both as teacher and as a painter. My friend says M. Duran takes more interest in each of his pupils . . . besides I admired Duran's pictures immensely in the salon and he is considered one of the greatest French artists'.

The atelier system was the backbone of French art education and at this time was dominated by those of Cabanel and Gérôme. Carolus-Duran's had started in 1872 and was run by the students on democratic lines. Most were Anglo-Saxons, and Sargent was evidently pleased with his choice for he wrote to the same friend again on 12 June: 'It is now almost three weeks since I entered the atelier of M. Carolus-Duran, a young and rising artist whose reputation is continually increasing. He is chiefly a portrait painter and has a very broad powerful and realistic style. I am quite delighted with the atelier, where, with the exception of two nasty little fat Frenchmen, the pupils are all gentlemanly, nice fellows . . . Duran comes regularly twice a week to our atelier (which is a more private affair and through which he gets no pecuniary remuneration) and carefully and thoroughly criticises the pupils' work, staying a short time with each one. He generally paints a newcomer's first study, as a lesson, and, as my first head had rather too sinister a charm, suggesting immoderate use of ivory blacks, he entirely repainted the face, and in about five minutes made a fine thing out of it and I keep it as such . . .'

Carolus-Duran was the most important influence on Sargent's early career.

Fig.12 Mrs Henry White (see no.12). From A. Nevins, *Henry White* (1930)

He had risen to fame in 1869 with the portrait of his wife, *La Femme au Gant*. Here the elements of dramatic power and realism were married to the technique of Velazquez in which tonal contrasts were subtly and absolutely controlled. Carolus-Duran's art, like that of Manet, had been transformed by the discovery of Velazquez, and, as a result, he was considered one of the avant-garde among the artists of Paris. Nevertheless, he enjoyed a huge success as a fashionable portrait painter. His principal concern was for total accuracy of vision: 'Search for the half-tones, place your accents, and then the lights . . . Velasquez, Velasquez, Velasquez, ceaselessly study Velasquez.' The technical precepts of Carolus-Duran can be studied when looking at *Head of Ana-Capri Girl* (no.3), and R. A. M. Stevenson's lucid description of painting a head in Duran's manner is discussed in the notes to this picture.

There are innumerable secondary influences at work in Sargent's early style: his admiration for other old masters, particularly the work of Frans Hals; his love of the exotic (a constant theme throughout his career), which produced *Fumée d'Ambre Gris* and *El Jaleo*; and his great interest in the effects of natural light.

Undoubtedly Sargent was ambitious for success, and the portrait of *Carolus-Duran* marked the beginning of his professional career. The development of a style of his own became apparent very soon afterwards, and Sargent's Paris career can be seen as a series of experiments away from the formula of his master. In this exhibition the closest example to a portrait in Duran's manner is that of *Edouard Pailleron* (no.5). More experimental are *The Daughters of Edward D. Boit* (no.10), showing an interest in both Velazquez and Frans Hals, and the small presentation portraits in an informal manner. *Madame X* (no.13) represents the last of these experiments: never to be repeated, it remains a masterpiece of painting and an extraordinary evocation of a phenomenom of the Third Republic – the professional beauty. The less sensational but faultless portrait of *Mrs Henry White* (no.12) represents the more acceptable image, and was to pave the way for the future.

Fig.13 In his Paris studio, c.1883

1 *Fanny Watts 1876*

Pencil on paper, 29.2 × 23 (11½ × 9)

Inscribed and dated in pencil in the artist's hand (bottom left): *St Enogat Jan 1st 1876*; inscribed, signed and dated (bottom right): *to my friend Fannie/John S. Sargent/London Feb 1907*

Provenance: The sitter; given to her goddaughter, and thence by descent

Lent anonymously

A drawing of Sargent's childhood friend in a Breton head-dress, drawn at St Enogat near Dinard on the Brittany coast. Sargent's parents had taken a house there, the Maison Lefort, in the summer of 1875 and stayed on through the winter. Writing to his friend Ben Castillo in June 1875, Sargent described the place (Charteris 1927, p.38): 'We enjoy our little country house very much with its pleasant gardens and thoroughly rural entourage. I have reason to be contented and thankful for my quarters are charming. My bedroom is the most beautiful interior I have ever seen in anything short of a palace or a castle. It is furnished throughout in the medieval style. Its beamed ceiling and floor are of oak, its walls completely hung with stamped leather and arras; the furniture is all antique and richly carved . . . Then there is a great tapestried chimney piece . . . This enumeration ends with the most charming detail of all; the windows. They are of lattice, that is to say, of small lozenges of glass, joined together by bands of lead, and from them you look right over and into the fig tree with its great shining green leaves and ripening fruit, then over the pear trees and cherry trees and flowers of the garden, to the wide cornfields, and over them to the sea'. It was probably at St Enogat that Sargent painted the ravishing early picture of *Two Wineglasses* (private collection).

Frances (Fanny or Fannie) Sherburne Ridley Watts (1858–1927) was the daughter of well-to-do American parents, who spent much of their time in Europe. Sargent had first met her in Florence or Nice, in that expatriate circle that included the Castillos and the Pagets (see no.33). Fanny was an attractive and vivacious girl, and Sargent remained devoted to her; there were even rumours of a romance. In 1877 he sent a threequarter-length oil of her (Philadelphia Museum) to the Salon, his first contribution. His early correspondence with her, which

1 *Fanny Watts*

has recently come to light, is written in an amusing and racy style and shows that they were close friends. It also offers new biographical information on the artist's life in Paris. In a letter of 10 March 1876, written from his studio at 19 Rue de l'Odéon, Sargent bemoaned the fact that she was not coming to Paris. He had hoped to receive her in his studio, 'offering you my own chaise & showing you my own work (without however blowing my own trumpet!) You and Em [his sister Emily] would I hoped come often & spend afternoons talking about last winter and last summer at old Dinard, or playing the piano, in short making yourself perfectly at home.'

Sargent remained close to Fanny all his life. They corresponded regularly, and she always visited him when she came to London. When she married Colonel Frederick White, the brother of the singer Maud White, late in life, Sargent gave her away, presenting her with this drawing as a wedding present, and perhaps also the picture of Capri (no.4). After the death of her husband, Fanny became increasingly unstable and ended her life in an asylum. For a later water-colour of her, see no.24.

2 *Two Boys on a Beach, Naples* (also called *Innocents Abroad*) *1878*

Oil on canvas, 26 × 34.3 (10 × 13½)

Provenance: The artist's sister, Violet Ormond; thence by family descent

Exhibitions: Tate Gallery 1926, cat. p.7; London 1926 (409), with wrong sizes, and under title *Little Boys: Naples*; Birmingham 1964 (3)

Literature: Mount 1969, p.460 (K788); Ormond 1970, p.235

Lent by the Ormond Family

In late July 1878, after the successful reception of his *plein-air* picture *Oyster Gatherers of Cancale* (Corcoran Gallery of Art, Washington DC) at the Salon, where it gained a second-class medal, Sargent left Paris for Capri. On the way he spent a week in Naples. In a letter from Capri to his old friend Ben Castillo (dated by Castillo 10 August 1878) he spoke of his time there (Charteris 1927, pp.47–8): 'Naples is simply superb and I spent a delightful week there. Of course it was very hot, and one generally feels used up. It is a fact that in Naples they

2 *Two Boys on a Beach, Naples*

eke out their wine with spirits and drugs, so that a glass of wine and water at a meal will make a man feel drunk. I had to take bad beer in order not to feel good-for-nothing. I could not sleep at night. In the afternoon I would smoke a cigarette in an armchair or on my bed and at five o'clock wake up suddenly from a deep sleep of several hours. Then lie awake all night and quarrel with mosquitoes, fleas, and all imaginable beasts. I am frightfully bitten from head to foot. Otherwise Italy is all that one can dream for beauty and charm.'

It was presumably during this week that Sargent painted this sketch, possibly as a preliminary for a slightly more highly finished picture, also entitled *Innocents Abroad* (Sterling and Francine Clark Art Institute, Williamstown), which contains an additional two figures. The latter is signed and dated 1879, which may indicate that it was completed in studio conditions after Sargent's return to Paris, in much the same way as *Oyster Gatherers of Cancale*.

The picture of *Two Boys on a Beach, Naples* is an exercise in the effect of direct sunlight on sand and sea with the figures of the children exposed to the strong heat of the sun. The handling of the picture is extremely sketchy, the brushwork bold and

summary with touches of impasto suggesting the foam of the waves and pools of water in the foreground. The spontaneous character of this sketch, which gives it so much of its charm, is somehow lost in the more contrived figures of the larger picture.

This subject is strongly related to *Oyster Gatherers of Cancale*, but a comparison of the two indicates Sargent's sensitivity to different light conditions. The former carefully evokes the sunlight of an Atlantic sky while this is unmistakably Mediterranean. The figures in the Washington picture are arranged as a procession with their heads silhouetted against the sky which occupies half of the picture plane, while here the figures are depicted against the deeper colours of the beach, the sea and the horizon. *Oyster Gatherers* was a conscious attempt to create a popular genre picture for the Salon, while this is less obviously a subject picture.

Another nude child on a beach cast in shadow, with the sea and two cliffs in strong sunlight in the background, is in the Ormond family collection and belongs to this period. A similar subject, *A Summer Idyll*, is in the Brooklyn Museum.

3 *Head of Ana-Capri Girl 1878*

Oil on wood, 22.9 × 25.4 (9 × 10)

Provenance: The artist's sister, Emily Sargent; thence by family descent

Exhibitions: Tate Gallery 1926, cat. p.9; London 1926 (218)

Literature: *Scribner's Magazine*, XXXIV (1903), p.529, repr.; repr. Meynell 1903, 1927; Downes 1925, p.172; G. P. Jacomb-Hood, 'John Sargent', *Cornhill Magazine*, NS LIX (1925), p.282; Charteris 1927, repr. facing p.48; Mount 1969, p.459 (783); Mckibbin 1956, p.120; Ormond 1970, p.236

Lent by the Ormond Family

3 *Head of Ana-Capri Girl*

In the same letter to Ben Castillo in which Sargent described his experiences at Naples and his crossing to Capri (see no.2), he ends, 'I am painting away very hard and shall be here a long time.' (Charteris 1927, p.48.) At first Sargent was without the companionship which was such a feature of studio life in Paris. 'If it were not for one German staying at the Marina, I should be absolutely without society and he is in love and cannot talk about anything but his sweetheart's moral irreproachability. We are going over to Sorrento in a day or two to visit her, and I have agreed to keep her husband's interest rivetted to Vesuvius, Baiae, Pozzuoli and other places along the distant opposite shore.'

Although the island had not yet become a Mecca for international personalities, there were a number of English and French artists spending the summer there. One of these, Frank Hyde, invited Sargent to share his working quarters in the old monastery of Santa Lucia. Here he met the famous model Rosina, 'an Ana-Capri girl, a magnificent type, about seventeen years of age, her complexion a rich nut-brown, with a mass of blue-black hair, very beautiful, and of an Arab type.' (Charteris 1927, p.48.)

This brilliant profile relates to the finished picture *Dans les Oliviers à Capri* which exists in two versions (Museum of Fine Arts, Boston, and a private collection), one of which was exhibited at the Salon 1879. The figure in the finished picture is seen in full length with her back to the spectator and her face in profile looking to the right; her body rests on the branch of a tree.

This sketch is a particularly fine example of the technique of painting as taught by Carolus-Duran and recounted by R. A. M. Stevenson: 'After a slight search of proportions with charcoal, the places of masses were indicated with a rigger dipped in flowing pigment. No preparation in colour or monochrome was allowed, but the main planes of the face must be laid directly on the unprepared canvas with a broad brush. These few surfaces – three or four in the forehead, as many in the nose, and so forth, must be studied in shape and place, and particularly in the relative value of light that their various inclinations produce. They were painted quite broadly in even tones of flesh tint, and stood side by side like pieces of a mosaic, without fusion of their adjacent edges. No brushing of the edge of the hair into the face was permitted, no conventional bounding of eyes and features with lines that might deceive the student by their expression into the belief that false structure was truthful. In the next stage you were bound to proceed in the same manner by laying planes upon the

junctions of the larger ones or by breaking the larger planes into subordinate surfaces. You were never allowed to brush one surface into another, you must make a tone for each step of a gradation.' (R. A. M. Stevenson, *Velazquez*, 1895, p.105.)

All the problems inherent in a profile of this type have been squarely faced by Sargent and the result is an almost text-book example of his master's style, and the effect is strikingly sculptural. Rosina was certainly a physical type to which Sargent responded brilliantly and many of his most memorable portraits are of women of mysterious dark beauty: *Madame Gautreau*, *La Carmencita*, *Lady Agnew*, the *Nude Egyptian Girl*, not to mention his many Semitic subjects. Sargent painted at least two other sketches of her in full face.

Jacomb-Hood, a neighbour of Sargent's in later years in Chelsea, remembered this sketch in his memoir of Sargent. He described it as 'Holbeinesque in its severe and clean outline and subtle modelling.'

4 *Capri 1878*

Oil on canvas, 51 × 63.5 (20 × 25)

Inscribed and signed (bottom left): *to my friend Fanny/John S. Sargent*; inscribed (bottom right): *Capri 1878*

Provenance: Given by the artist to Miss Fanny Watts, perhaps as a wedding present, 1907; inherited by Miss Watts's goddaughter; thence by descent

Lent anonymously

The picture shows Sargent's favourite Capri model, Rosina (see no.3), dancing on a rooftop, accompanied by a girl singing, with a tambourine. Charteris records that during his stay on the island Sargent organized a fête with other artists 'at which the tarantella was danced on the flat roof of his hotel, to an orchestra of tambourines and guitars' (Charteris 1927, p.48). Perhaps this picture, and another almost identical version (formerly Knoedler), are a reminiscence of that occasion. The composition is a daring one, dominated by the flat side wall of the house. But there is poetry in the way the evening sunlight catches the rooftops and lights up the exultant figure of the dancer. The moon rises on the left above a dark green hillside dotted with houses. Rosina's mauvish-pink overskirt is a telling accent in this otherwise muted and sensitive colour scheme. The picture certainly anticipates the theme and pose of Sargent's famous painting of a Spanish dancer, *El Jaleo* (Salon, 1882; Isabella Stewart Gardner Museum, Boston).

Fanny Watts (see no.1) was an intimate friend of the young Sargent, who contributed a portrait of her to the Salon of 1877. The form of the signature, however, clearly belongs to a later date than the original inscription, 'Capri 1878'; the picture may well have been a wedding present, as the drawing of Fanny in a Breton head-dress of 1876 in the same collection is inscribed as being.

5 *Edouard Pailleron 1879*

Colour plate 1, facing page 8

Oil on canvas, 128 × 96 (50 × 37)

Signed (bottom left): *John S. Sargent*

Provenance: Given to the Musée National, Versailles, by Madame Edouard Pailleron

Exhibition: Paris 1963 (2), repr.

4 *Capri*

Literature: Charteris 1927, p.258 (incorrectly dated 1880); A. Lalia-Paternostro, *Edouard Pailleron* (Paris, 1931), frontis.; M-L. Pailleron, *Le Paradis Perdu* (Paris, 1947), p.154, repr.; Mckibbin 1956, p.115 (incorrectly dated 1878); C. M. Mount, *Art Quarterly*, xx (1957), pp.304–5; Mount 1969, p.447 (795); Ormond 1970, p.18

Lent by the Musée National, Versailles.

5 *Edouard Pailleron*

Edouard Pailleron (1834–99) was a celebrated poet and dramatist. He was educated for the Bar, but after pleading a single case he entered the Army. He travelled in North Africa with the artist Beaucé, and on his return to Paris produced a volume of satires entitled *Les Paracites*. In 1862 he married Marie Buloz, daughter of Edmond Buloz, editor of the influential journal *Revue des Deux Mondes*. In 1881 his most successful play, *Le Monde ou l'on s'ennuie*, was produced. It was a brilliant comedy, ridiculing contemporary academic society and filled with transparent allusions to well-known people.

By 1879 Sargent was frequenting several literary and musical salons in Paris, including that of Madame Roger-Jourdain.

Mount suggests that it may have been here that he met Pailleron. Marie-Louise Pailleron, the sitter's daughter, wrote a lengthy account of Sargent in her memoirs, *Le Paradis Perdu* (op.cit.), and recalled that her parents began seeing Sargent in their house in Quai Malquais where they entertained a large number of artists. In an interview, Monsieur Robert Bourget Pailleron thought that his grandfather had been impressed with reports of Sargent's fame and considered him to be the leader of a new generation (Mount 1969, p.59 ff.). He was certainly impressed with Sargent's knowledge of French literature and music. At all events, Emily Sargent wrote to Vernon Lee on 9 August 1879: 'He has just painted the portrait of Ed. Pailleron' (Colby College).

The portrait of Edouard Pailleron represents one of Sargent's most important early commissions and was undoubtedly the result of the successful reception of *Carolus-Duran* (1879; Sterling and Francine Clark Art Institute, Williamstown), exhibited at the Salon in 1879, to which this portrait is closely related. Dr Sargent wrote from St Gervais, Savoy, on 15 August 1879: '. . . But as the proof of the pudding is in the eating, so the best, or one of the best evidences of a portrait's success is the receiving by the artist of commissions to execute others. And John received six such evidences from French people. He was very busy during the two months we were in Paris.'

Stylistically the portrait of Edouard Pailleron is close to that of Carolus-Duran's painting. He is posed in an attitude of studied informality, unmistakably the figure of a successful Gallic *litterateur*. The penetrating gaze suggests a high intelligence and the face is evidently that of a man of powerful creative gifts. This contrasts brilliantly with the untidy shirt, the dog-eared pages of the book and the gesture of the index finger of his left hand. Sargent's portrait of *Madame Edouard Pailleron* (Corcoran Gallery of Art, Washington DC), painted later that summer in the garden of the Buloz country house, is a significant departure from this style in its treatment of the figure in a landscape.

6 *A Venetian Interior*

6 *A Venetian Interior* c.*1880*

Water-colour and pencil on paper,
50.8 × 35.5 (20 × 14)

Provenance: The artist's sister, Violet
Ormond; thence by family descent

Exhibition: *Venice Rediscovered*, Wildenstein,
London, 1972 (38)

Literature: Ormond 1970, p.69

Lent by the Ormond Family

This is closely related to the group of
interior oils discussed with no.9, but it
appears to be the only study to have
survived in water-colour. The location
appears to be the ground floor of a Venetian
palazzo with the viewpoint towards the
Canal. The same obsessions are present: the
steeply receding perspective and the distant
light-source, supplemented by an oblique
opening to the left. The centrally placed
figure, looking down at her work, and the
predominant dark tonality add to the sense
of mystery. Particularly effective is the use
of the white of the paper to indicate the
brilliant lighting in the background – a
device Sargent was to use again during his
most prolific period as a water-colour
painter.

7 *Unfinished Sketch of a Lady in a Gondola* c.*1881*

Water-colour and pencil on paper, 33 × 24
(13 × 9½)

Provenance: The artist's sister, Violet
Ormond; thence by family descent

Lent by the Ormond Family

This sketch was probably made on Sargent's
visit to Venice in 1880 or 1882. The identity
of the figure has not been ascertained, but
she conforms in type to the black-shawled
models used by the artist in his oils (see
no.9).

There are a number of water-colours
belonging to Sargent's adolescence and to
the 1880s, but it is not until after 1900 that
he used this medium on an extensive scale.
The subjects of these early works tend to be
architectural studies, but there are a small
number in which the figures predominate
(see no.6). The earliest water-colours tend
to be rather laboured in execution, but by
1880 it is evident that he had realized the
inherent quality of directness and rapidity

to which water-colour lends itself.

In this picture it is possible to see the
artist's technique at work: the face is
brilliantly finished while the folds of the
drapery are suggested with immense rapidity and freedom. In the background a blue
haze and a few outlines in pencil suggest
the architecture, while the figure of the
gondolier and the prow of the boat are
indicated by pencil. Most of the foreground
is untouched, which gives an impression
that the figure is suspended in space.

8 *Poppy Graeme* *1881*

Oil on canvas, 56.5 × 43.2 (22¼ × 17)

Inscribed and signed (upper left and right):
to my friend Farquharson John S. Sargent

Provenance: Presented to Aberdeen Art
Gallery by Joseph Farquharson, R.A., 1934

Literature: Mount 1969, p.440 (811);
Mckibbin 1956, p.98; Aberdeen Art
Gallery, *Permanent Collection Catalogue* (1968),
p.87

Lent by Aberdeen Art Gallery and Museums

Poppy Graeme was a relative of the artist
Joseph Farquharson, and this portrait was
painted by way of thanks for Sargent's stay
in London in 1881. (Letter in Aberdeen Art
Gallery and Museums archives.)

Sargent came to London in the summer of
1881 when the rest of his family sailed for
America, and he stayed at the studio of his
friend Joseph Farquharson, who was in
Egypt. The Sargent family had first met
Farquharson in the summer of 1868 at Mürren
when John was aged twelve, and Farquharson
had given Sargent his first lessons in
portrait drawing. The friendship was undoubtedly renewed when Farquharson
became an occasional student at the
Carolus-Duran studio, and this was maintained until Sargent's death.

Mckibbin states that this sketch was
executed in 1881 at Farquharson's studio in
London, where Sargent had gone in June to
paint two heads. Mount says that these
were not commissioned portraits but gifts to
friends and were three in number. (*Art
Quarterly*, XX, 1957, p.312.) These three are
the exhibited portrait, the portrait of
Robert Farquharson (brother of Joseph) which
was painted in Finzean in Scotland
(Aberdeen Art Gallery), and the well known
Vernon Lee (Tate Gallery, London).

Vernon Lee's *Letters* (edited by Irene

7 *Unfinished Sketch of a Lady in a Gondola*

8 *Poppy Graeme*

Cooper Willis, privately printed, 1937) are a constant source of information concerning Sargent in the early 1880s. She had not met Sargent for nine years until their encounter in London in 1881 at the house of her friend Mary Robinson in Gower Street. She wrote to her mother on 16 June 1881: 'When we returned home, the maid said there were visitors in the drawing room, Mr Sargent – so I rushed up to John and past two others . . . John is very stiff, a sort of completely accentless mongrel, not at all like Curtis or Newman; rather French faubourg sort of manners . . . He was very shy, having I suppose a vague sense that there were poets about.' (Cooper Willis, op.cit. p.61.) They also visited Burne Jones's studio: 'Some of Burne Jones pictures especially a set of unfinished things of the Sleeping Beauty, I admired extremely, & so did John; I think John is singularly unprejudiced, almost too amiably candid in his judgements. He remained to tea . . . He talked art and literature, just as formerly, and then, quite unbidden, sat down to the piano & played all sorts of bits of things, ends & middles of things, just as when he was a boy.' (Cooper Willis, op.cit. p.63.)

Poppy Graeme is seen in near profile with an intense light cast from the lower right which causes her nose to stand out in relief against the shadows of the left cheek. The modelling of the head is somewhat dramatic, but reaches great subtlety in her lower chin and dimple. Sargent has used the boldest strokes of paint to suggest the fur collar of her coat and the light on her hair.

This painting belongs to a significant group of sketches painted from c.1877 to 1894, mainly portraits of artists or friends. They include sketches of *Paul Helleu* (1877; private collection), *Madame Buloz* (1879; private collection), *Henri Lefort* (1881; St Louis Museum), *Mrs Curtis* (no.11) and *Madame Allouard-Jouan* (Petit Palais, Paris). In general the faces emerge from dark backgrounds with a great emphasis on individual characteristics. Possibly the most famous of these is the well-known *Vernon Lee* (Tate Gallery, London), painted in three hours on 23 June 1881. Equally appealing is the chic *Madame Paul Escudier* (Sterling and Francine Clark Art Institute, Williamstown) or the slightly intense *Charles Stewart Forbes* (c.1889; private collection).

Only a few of Sargent's portrait sketches have survived, but he undoubtedly painted a very large number. Miss Heyneman, a pupil of his in later years, remembered his

advice: 'Paint a hundred studies . . . Sketch everything and keep your curiosity fresh' (Charteris 1927, p.185).

9 *Venetian Bead Stringers*
c.*1880–2*

Oil on canvas, 67.2 × 78.1 (26⅜ × 30¾)

Signed (top right): *John S. Sargent*

Provenance: Bought from the artist by the Albright-Knox Art Gallery, 1917

Exhibitions: Possibly Grosvenor Gallery, London, 1882 (135 or 346); Society of American Artists, New York, 1893; Copley Hall, Boston, 1899 (37); American Artists, Buffalo, 1913; Grand Central Galleries, New York, 1924 (52); Washington 1964 (21) repr.

Literature: *Scribner's Magazine*, XXXIV, (1903), p.520; Downes 1925, pp.144–5; Charteris 1927, p.283; Mount, *Art Quarterly*, 1963, fig.13; Mount 1969, p.463 (K826); Ormond 1970, pp.29, 238, plate 21

Lent by the Albright-Knox Art Gallery, Buffalo, NY (Friends of the A. A. G. Fund)

Sargent visited Venice in the late summer and autumn of 1880 and again in 1882. In 1880 he travelled with his family, staying at the Hotel de l'Italie, Piazza San Moise, until they returned to Nice and then at 290 Piazza San Marco, All 'Orologio. He found a studio in Palazzo Rezzonico which was being occupied by a number of artists of his acquaintance, including Whistler and Boldini. On his visit in 1882 he stayed with the Curtis family at Palazzo Barbaro (see no.11).

This picture is one of an interesting small group of paintings executed in Venice either in 1880 or 1882, or possibly later. The interior scenes represent similar figures either at work or nonchalantly standing about. They are seen in the same long corridor of the *piano nobile* of an unidentified palace with steeply receding perspectives. They are characterized by a subdued tonality mostly of browns and blacks and a great interest in the effects of oblique light sources, often broken by the use of blinds or slats, creating a distilled atmosphere and an overall impression of melancholy. The exterior scenes, notably *A Street in Venice* (National Gallery of Art, Washington DC) and *Venetian Street Scene* (Sterling and

Francine Clark Art Institute, Williamstown) also represent similar technical features: rather blurred foregrounds, focusing on the figures in the middle distance, and a strong sense of geometrical forms, deriving from Velazquez.

This picture is most closely related to *Venetian Interior* (Sterling and Francine Clark Art Institute, Williamstown) and the *Venetian Interior* (Carnegie Institute, Pittsburgh), in that they are all occupied by the same female figures in a long corridor. The view-point in this picture is almost identical to that of the Williamstown picture, although the latter contains at least four more figures. In all three they are draped in black shawls and are silhouetted against the whitewashed wall, reminiscent of *El Jaleo* (1882). The main source of light here comes from the three openings in the background and the doorway to the left. The composition of the staircase from which this comes diffuses the light into the room where the figures are seen in the foreground.

The problem of dating Sargent's Venetian pictures to the years 1880 or 1882 or later is complicated owing to the consistency in his style. It is clear that he exhibited two Venetian interiors at the Grosvenor Gallery in 1882 and since this exhibition opened in May, well before his departure to Venice, they must have been executed on the 1880 visit. Unfortunately no description of the exhibited pictures has come to light in order to identify them further. The evidence of another artist in Venice in 1880, Luke Fildes, does nothing to help: 'His [Sargent's] colour is black, but very strong painting.' (L. V. Fildes, *A Victorian Painter*, 1958, p.67.) Two unrelated pictures depicting the Venetian model Gigia Viani are signed and dated 1882 and at least one exterior scene – *A Street in Venice* (National Gallery of Art, Washington DC) – was shown at the first exhibition of the Société Internationale des Peintres et Sculpteurs, Rue de Sèze, in 1883 and illustrated in the *Gazette des Beaux Arts*. Mount dates this picture to 1882, while Ormond suggests 1880 if it was exhibited at the Grosvenor Gallery in 1882, but points out that Sargent may have carried over his subjects, settings and models from one visit to the next.

Sargent's response to Venice at this time is in marked contrast to the other artists who descended on the city each summer to explore the possibilities of *genre* in the canals and by-ways. Royal Cortissoz spoke of this aspect of Sargent's work: 'You enter a

9 *Venetian Bead Stringers*

10 *The Daughters of Edward D. Boit*

totally different world when you enter his Venice. But don't imagine for a moment that it is a negligible world. On the contrary, Sargent's Venice is one of the most interesting that I know. I remember a Venetian street scene of his, another picture of an interior with bead stringers at work . . .' ('Venice as a Painting Ground', *Personalities in Art*, New York, 1925, pp.118–19). It is possible that this group of pictures are preparations for an intended Salon painting which never materialised.

10 *The Daughters of Edward D. Boit 1882*

Oil on canvas, 221 × 221 (87 × 87)

Signed and dated (bottom right): *John S. Sargent 1882*

Provenance: Given to the Museum of Fine Arts, Boston, by the daughters of Edward D. Boit in memory of their father, 1919

Exhibitions: Société Internationale des Peintres et Sculpteurs, Rue de Sèze, Paris, 1883; Salon, 1883 (2165); St Botolph Club, Boston, 1888; Exposition Universelle, Paris, 1900; Boston 1925 (20); New York 1926 (7), repr.; *Sargent, Whistler and Mary Cassatt*, Art Institute of Chicago and elsewhere, 1954 (47), repr.; Boston 1956 (4), repr.

Literature: *L'Art*, XXXIII (1883), p.118; *Art Amateur*, IX (1883), p.46; *Gazette des Beaux Arts*, XXVII (1883), p.190, and XXVIII (1883), p.9; *Magazine of Art* (1883), pp.497–8; *Nouvelle Revue*, XXII (1883), pp.714–15; *Revue des Deux Mondes*, LVII (1883), p.616; *Harper's New Monthly Magazine*, LXXV (1887), p.690, repr.; *Century Magazine*, LII (1896), p.175; *Magazine of Art*, XXII (1899), p.115, repr.; *International Studio*, X (1900), pp.18–19; repr. Meynell 1903, 1927; *Scribner's Magazine*, XXXIV (1903), p.528; *MFA Bulletin*, X (1912), p.21, and XVII (1919), p.49; Downes 1925, pp.11, 130–1; Charteris 1927, pp.57–8, 258; *Art News*, LIII (1954), p.61; Mckibbin 1956, p.85; Henry James, *The Painter's Eye*, ed. J. L. Sweeney (1956), pp.222–3; E. P. Richardson, *Painting in America* (1956), p.282; Mount, *Art Quarterly*, 1963, pp.398–9, repr.; Mount 1969, pp.281, 366, 432 (8211); *American Paintings in the Museum of Fine Arts, Boston* (1969), I, pp.225–6, and II, fig.454; Ormond 1970, pp.27, 29, 30, 31, 239, plates 25, V and cover (detail)

Lent by the Museum of Fine Arts, Boston

(Gift of Mary Louisa Boit, Julia Overing Boit, Jane Hubbard Boit and Florence D. Boit, in memory of their father)

The Sargents were well acquainted with the Boit family, whose father, Edward D. Boit, was a painter and a prominent figure in the expatriate American community of Paris and Rome. His daughters were (from left to right) Mary Louisa, Florence, Jane and Julia, and the portrait was painted in the family apartment in Paris.

This well-known group represents many of Sargent's preoccupations of the years in which he was developing a style independent of Carolus-Duran. In terms of composition the picture is closely related to Velazquez's *Las Meninas*, which Sargent had copied on his visit to Spain in 1879 (Ormond family), and in terms of facture it shows a continued interest in the technique of Frans Hals. While he was in Venice in 1880–2 he had also experimented with certain pictorial features (see no. 9) which are brought to bear in this portrait. The composition is based on strong geometrical accents and the figures are illuminated from an oblique light-source. The little girl with her doll in the foreground is exposed to the full brilliance of the light streaming in from the left, but the handling is blurred, thereby inviting the spectator to examine the more closely observed sisters behind. There is a sense of mystery which pervades the group (not unlike the *Pailleron Children*, 1881; Armand J. Hammer collection), and a deliberate lack of relationship between the figures.

All these factors had been individually explored in smaller-scale works, but it is only in this one picture that they are brought together for the purpose of a large portrait group to be exhibited at the Salon. A new feature is the careful disposition of the masses and the use of props, namely the enormous blue-and-white vases (still owned by a member of the family), the two vases on a mantelpiece in the background, the mirror behind them reflecting the window, and the enveloping *savonnerie* carpet, for highly controlled effects. The combination of devices used here is not seen again in Sargent's oeuvre, and his later informal group portraits (eg *The Sitwell Family*, 1900; private collection) are more properly described as conversation pieces. Nor was he to depict figures again with quite the same quality of ethereal abstraction in their expressions.

The critics at the Salon realized the painting's unconventionality. The *Revue des Deux Mondes* described it as 'composed according to some new rules; the rules of the four corners game' ('composé d'après des règles nouvelles; les règles du jour des quatre coins').

Henry James, who first met Sargent through Mrs Boit, was to give a glowing report of it in *Harper's Magazine*: 'The artist has done nothing more felicitous and interesting than this view of a rich, dim, rather generalized French interior (the perspective of a hall with a shining floor, where screens and tall Japanese vases shimmer and loom), which encloses the life and seems to form the happy play-world of a family of charming children. The treatment is eminently unconventional, and there is none of the usual symmetrical balancing of the figures in the foreground. The place is regarded as a whole; it is a scene, a comprehensive impression; yet none the less do the little figures in their white pinafores (when was the pinafore ever painted with that power and made so poetic?) detach themselves and live with a personal life. Two of the sisters stand hand in hand at the back, in the delightful, the almost equal, company of a pair of immensely tall emblazoned jars, which overtop them and seem also to partake of the life of the picture; the splendid porcelain and the aprons of the children shine together, while the mirror in the brown depth behind them catches the light. Another little girl presents herself, with abundant tresses and slim legs, her hands behind her, quite to the left; and the youngest, nearest to the spectator, sits on the floor and plays with her doll. The naturalness of the composition, the loveliness of the complete effect, the light, free security of the execution, the sense it gives us as of assimilated secrets and of instinct and knowledge playing together – all this makes the picture as astonishing a work on the part of a young man of twenty-six as the portrait of 1881 [*Lady with a Rose*] was astonishing on the part of a young man of twenty-four.' (James, op.cit.)

11 *Mrs Daniel Sargent Curtis 1882*

Oil on canvas, 71.1 × 53.3 (28 × 21)

Dated (upper left): *Venice 1882*; signed and inscribed (upper right): *John S. Sargent/ to my kind friend Mrs Curtis*

Provenance: By family descent; Samuel H. Kress; given to the University of Kansas, 1963

Exhibitions: Possibly Société Internationale des Peintres et Sculpteurs, Rue de Sèze, Paris, 1883; Boston 1956 (5), repr.; *Images: 23 Interpretations*, Kansas, 1964

Literature: *Gazette des Beaux Arts*, NS I (1883), p.190; Mckibbin 1956, p.91, fig.16; Mount 1969, pp.71, 435 (822); Ormond 1970, pp.21, 239–40, plate 28

Lent by the Helen Foresman Spencer Museum of Art, University of Kansas (Samuel H. Kress Study Collection)

Mrs Curtis, née Ariana Wormely, was the daughter of an English admiral and married Daniel Curtis, who was a cousin of Dr Sargent. Their son Ralph was a close friend of Sargent's and they were contemporaries at Carolus-Duran's studio.

The Curtis family were of New England extraction but lived mainly in Europe and were in constant touch with the Sargent family. In 1878, when Palazzo Barbaro on the Grand Canal in Venice was divided, the Curtises took the major portion of the building, which is still in their possession. They returned to Venice from their travels each spring and received a large number of visitors (many introduced through Sargent), including Henry James, Isabella Stewart Gardner and Vernon Lee. The latter described her first visit there in September 1885: 'It seems John had mentioned my arrival in a letter. They made me come upstairs, & return to dinner, & sent me back in their gondola. They were indeed most friendly & amiable. Mr Curtis is a nice brisk little man, rather timidly anxious to put in a little piece of information or an anecdote or joke here & there; his wife is of the rather die-away English American, & is pathetic over the omnibus steamers which ply up and down the Grand Canal; but she is also very amiable . . . These sort of Americans, who shudder at Howells, look up to [Henry] James as a sort of patron saint of cosmopolitan refinement. Their apartment (they go about from place to place in winter) is on the 2nd floor of P/o Barbaro, a beautiful palace on the Canal & next to Palazzo Cavalli, where Chambord used to live. It is a vast & luxurious & exquisite place, full of beautiful furniture and pictures & at the same time absolutely unpretentious . . .' (*Vernon Lee's Letters*, ed. I. Cooper Willis, 1937, p.202.) Henry

11 *Mrs Daniel Sargent Curtis*

James was to use the palace as the Venetian setting in *The Wings of the Dove*.

Mrs Curtis was a woman of great charm and personality and became known as the *dogaressa*. She could, however, be forthright in her judgements, and she rejected Sargent's well-known *Venetian Interior* (1899; Royal Academy), which evokes the setting of Palazzo Barbaro so brilliantly, as she considered the figure of her son Ralph lounging about on a baroque table to be indecorous. She also disliked being made to look her age. Another example of her fastidiousness was when they cold-shouldered Vernon Lee in Venice in 1890, possibly as a result of 'that story "Two Novels" . . . which may have been represented as a skit on all Venetian society.' (Cooper Willis, op.cit. pp.323, 324.)

The portrait of Mrs Curtis belongs to the group of informal paintings presented by Sargent to friends over the period circa 1877 to 1893 (see no.8) which are mainly characterized by bravura brushstrokes and a strong sense of the personality of the sitter. In this case the boldness of the handling is more restrained and the head is seen in a strong light against a completely dark background. This portrait may have been exhibited, together with the *Boit Children* (no.10) and *Vernon Lee* (Tate Gallery, London), at the exhibition of the Société Internationale des Peintres et Sculpteurs, Rue de Sèze, Paris, 1883, where the re-

viewer in the *Gazette des Beaux Arts*, Arthur Baignères, wrote of two portraits: 'l'un de femme en noir qui est tout éclatant, enlevé de main de maître.' The profile is enormously effective owing to the light-source shining on the subject's furthest cheek. The concept of the truncated head-and-shoulders which gives the picture its sculptural quality could well derive from Giovanni Bellini's *Doge Loredano* (National Gallery, London).

Sargent stayed with the Curtises at Palazzo Barbaro from about August 1882 until he returned to Paris in the late autumn or winter. He was to stay with them on many subsequent visits to Venice.

12 *Mrs Henry White 1883*

Colour plate II, between pages 8 and 9

Oil on canvas, 222 × 140 (87 × 55)

Signed and dated (lower right): *John S. Sargent 1883*

Provenance: By descent; given to the Corcoran Gallery of Art by John Campbell White

Exhibitions: R.A., 1884 (788); Exposition Universelle, Paris, 1900; Sixth exhibition of contemporary American paintings, Corcoran Gallery of Art, Washington DC, 1916–17; Grand Central Galleries, New York, 1924 (41); Washington, 1964 (24)

Literature: *Art Journal* (1884), p.242; *Athenaeum*, no.2956 (1884), p.798; *Graphic* (7 June 1884), p.562; *Saturday Review*, LII (1884), p.641; *The Times* (12 May 1884), p.4; R. A. M. Stevenson, 'J. S. Sargent', *Art Journal* (1888), p.68, repr.; Downes 1925, p.135; Charteris 1927, pp.66–8, 138, 259; A. Nevins, *Henry White* (New York, 1930), p.40; Henry James, *The Painter's Eye*, ed. J. L. Sweeney (1956), p.226; Mckibbin 1956, p.131; Mount, *Art Quarterly*, 1963, p.408, fig.31; Mount 1969, pp.76, 93, 95, 118, 286, 456 (836); Ormond 1970, pp.31, 33, 241–2, col. plate VI and plate 40; Adeline R. Tinter, 'Sargent in the Fiction of Henry James,' *Apollo*, CII (1975), pp.128–32, repr.; Larry J. Curry, 'Madame Paul Poirson: an Early Portrait by Sargent', *Bulletin of the Detroit Institute of Arts*, LI (1972), pp.99–100, repr.

Lent by the Corcoran Gallery of Art, Washington DC

Mrs Henry White, nee Margaret ('Daisy')

Stuyvesant Rutherford, was the daughter of Lewis Morris Rutherford of New York and New Jersey, a noted astronomer. She married the prominent American diplomat and was well known for her good looks and her intellectual character although she was slightly reserved by nature. According to A. Nevins, it was Sargent's 'fine portrait of Miss Burckhardt which determined the Whites to give him the commission', while Henry White sat to the more established artist Leon Bonnat.

The Whites were some of the first really well-off international patrons for whom Sargent worked. Hitherto his clientele had mostly come from a limited French avant-garde circle or through connections of long-standing acquaintance. The portrait of Mrs Henry White, painted in the new studio at Boulevard Berthier, was soon destined for their dining-room in Grosvenor Crescent, when Henry White became First Secretary to the American Embassy in London. Hung there 'it fulfilled a missionary and educational purpose, making the name of Sargent familiar to many and gradually enrolling supporters to a new canon of taste in portraiture.' (Charteris 1927, p.66.) The success of this picture was fundamental to Sargent's future career in England and America, all the more important since the failure of *Madame X* (no.13).

The portrait of *Madame X* has often been quoted as showing Sargent's interest in fifteenth-century Italian art at this time, particularly in the severity of the pose and the emphatic outline of the profile. *Mrs Henry White* was being painted at the same time, and shows little of the same interests. It is more a continuation of the style of *Dr Pozzi* or *Madame Pailleron*, but obviously less daring in pose and more in keeping with the decorum required of his patrons. At one level it is 'chic personified in paint,' at another it is the culmination of Sargent's Paris career and looks forward to his London style.

Mrs White stands boldly upright in the centre of the picture with a closed fan in one hand and an hour-glass in the other. The figure has deliberately been elongated, and a chaise-longue, cutting across the background, emphasizes the space in which she has been placed. The personality of Mrs White is suggested in her forceful head and in the nervous way she holds the fan and hour-glass. But above all, the interest is in the effect of directed light falling over her

12 *Mrs Henry White*

cream-coloured satin dress and train, exploring the shimmering effects of the material and the cast shadows which emphasize the recessions into the picture plane.

This was the second picture by Sargent to be exhibited at the Royal Academy and its reception in London was mixed. Most of the critics were aware of Sargent's style, and also of the furore being created across the Channel on account of *Madame X*. The *Athenaeum* castigated it: '. . . the painting is almost metallic, the carnations are raw, there is no taste in the expression, air or modelling . . .' *The Times* said: 'The head is breathing with life, and, slight as the execution seems to be, the whole picture has been painted with great care', but, 'it is hard to admit . . . that Mr Sargent has this year done justice to his unquestioned talent.' The American press was enthusiastic, but perhaps the most significant praise came from a fellow pupil of Carolus-Duran, R. A. M. Stevenson, four years later: 'A glance at the Mrs White will reveal something of Mr Sargent's speaking and eloquent workmanship. It will show, too, that large and noble disposition of a picture which we admire so much in the old masters. The canvas is admirably filled, the qualities of tranquil

space, and crowded clamorous space, are tastefully balanced, and the accessories stand in most harmonious relations to the figure. The wavering silhouette of the figure, now firmly detached from, and now sliding off into its surroundings, may be followed with pleasure even if held upside down. It falls into a perfect scheme of decorative effect, and yet it relieves from its environment with all the consistency and variety of truth.'

13 *Madame X 1884*
(Madame Pierre Gautreau)

Oil on canvas, 220 × 110 (82½ × 43½)

Signed and dated (bottom right): *John S. Sargent 1884*

Provenance: Bought from the artist by the Metropolitan Museum of Art, New York, 1916 (Arthur H. Hearn Fund)

Exhibitions: Salon, 1884 (2150); Carfax Gallery, London, 1909; Panama-Pacific Exposition, San Francisco, 1915; New York 1926 (10)

Literature: *Academy*, XXV (14 June 1884), p.427; *L'Art*, XXXVII (1884), pp.13–14; *Art Journal* (1884), pp.179–80; *Gaulois-Salon*, no.653 (30 April 1884), p.3; *Gazette des Beaux Arts*, XXIX (1 June 1884), pp.483–4; *L'Illustration*, no.2149 (3 May 1884), p.290; *Revue des Deux Mondes*, LXIII (1 June 1884), p.589; *Saturday Review*, LII (7 June 1884), p.745; *The Times* (3 June 1884), p.8; *Studio* (1900), p.21; *Scribner's Magazine*, XXXIV (1903), pp.514, 524–6, repr.; repr. Meynell 1903, 1927; Downes 1925, pp.12, 133–4; Charteris 1927, pp.59–65, 67, 98, 165, 249, 250, 252; *Vernon Lee's Letters*, ed. I. Cooper Willis (1937), pp.143, 177; Mckibbin 1956, p.97; Mount, *Art Quarterly*, 1963, p.408; Mount 1969, pp.73–93, 96, 100, 109, 114, 115, 129, 131, 137, 197, 282–4, 286–7, 301, 328–9, 439 (848), repr.; R. Ormond, *Colby Library Quarterly*, IX (September 1970), pp.173–5; Ormond 1970, pp.22, 31, 32, 33, 41, 45, 56, 240, 242, 243, plate 39

Lent by the Metropolitan Museum of Art (Arthur H. Hearn Fund, 1916)

Exhibited Detroit only

Madame Pierre Gautreau, née Virginie Avegno, was born in Louisiana and came to Paris after the American Civil War. She was married to a successful banker and was a conspicuous figure in the beau-monde. The many stories of her love affairs were well known. Sargent probably met Madame

13 *Madame X*

Gautreau through Doctor Pozzi, with whom she is said to have had an affair and whom Sargent painted in 1881 (Armand J Hammer collection). She was certainly a type to which Sargent was immediately attracted, possessing dark good looks and an air of languid sensuality. He wrote to his friend Ben Castillo: 'I have a great desire to paint her portrait and have reason to think she would allow it and is waiting for someone to propose this homage to her beauty. If you are "bien avec elle" and will see her in Paris you might tell her that I am a man of *prodigious talent*.' (Charteris 1927, p.59.) After some preliminary sittings during the winter he wrote to Vernon Lee from Nice on 10 February 1883: 'In a few days I shall be back in Paris tackling my other "envoi", the portrait of a great beauty. Do you object to people who are fardées to the extent of being uniform lavender or blotting paper colour all over? If so you would not care for my sitter. But she has the most beautiful lines and if the lavender or chlorate-of-potash-lozenge colour be pretty in itself I shall be more than pleased' (Ormond family.) Sargent had certainly hoped to complete her portrait for the 1883 Salon, but it was not until later in the summer, while staying at the Gautreau's house in Brittany, that he was able to make any advances in the picture and even then he was 'struggling with the unpaintable beauty of Me G'.

Unquestionably Sargent had in mind a portrait which would be the culmination of his ever-increasing success at the Salon, both with the public and his fellow artists. In the event the picture turned out to be a flop and became the centre of a minor scandal. The events of the opening day were recounted by Ralph Curtis, who was with Sargent at the time: 'In 15 mins I saw no end of acquaintances and strangers, and heard every one say "où est le portrait Gautreau?" . . . He [Sargent] was very nervous about what he feared, but his fears were far exceeded by the facts of yesterday. There was a grande tapage before it all day. In a few minutes I found him dodging behind doors to avoid friends who looked grave . . . all the women jeer Ah voilà "la belle!" "Oh quelle horreur!" etc. I went home with him, and remained there while he went to see the Boits. Mme Gautreau and mère came to his studio "bathed in tears". I staved them off but the mother returned and caught him and made a fearful scene saying "Ma fille est perdue – tout Paris se moque d'elle. Mon

Colour plate VII
Mrs Carl Meyer and her Children
1896 (no.41)

Colour plate VIII
Mrs George Swinton 1896–7 (no.42)

14 Madame Gautreau

15 Madame Gautreau

genre sera force de se battre. Elle mourira de chagrin" etc. John replied that it was against all laws to retire a picture. He had painted her exactly as she was dressed, that nothing could be said of the canvas worse than had been said in print of her appearance...'

Public response to the picture centred on the impropriety of her *décolletage* and the strange lavender colour of her skin. The coy reference to her as Mme xxx in the catalogue did nothing to veil her identity. The critics either took the same line as the public or complained of the monochrome flesh tints. Alone of these de Fourcaud of the *Gazette des Beaux Arts* was able to perceive the true meaning of the picture. He recognized it as a masterpiece in the depiction of an 'idol', not only in the extreme severity and rhythm of the lines, but for the summary it presents of the psychology of a professional beauty, dressed, posed and with her whole outlook adjusted to the supreme purpose of her role.

The pictorial thought behind the final version of *Madame X* is discussed with the drawings (nos.14 and 15). In the final version the figure is highly isolated with the head in severe profile and the body in slight *contrapposto*. The strong directed lighting onto the flesh emphasizes the statuesque quality of the composition, while the rhythm of the arms acts as a foil to the stark and to-

tally static outline of the head. Evocations of *Madame X* can be found in some of Sargent's later work, in particular *Isabella Stewart Gardner* (Isabella Stewart Gardner Museum, Boston), the *Nude Egyptian Girl* (1891; Chicago Art Institute), *Mrs George Swinton* (no.42) and *Ena and Betty Wertheimer* (no. 46). This picture remained in the artist's possession until 1916, as it had never been commissioned by the sitter. Sargent always considered it the finest thing he had ever painted. An unfinished replica was made later and is in the Tate Gallery.

14 *Madame Gautreau* c.*1883*
(two studies)

Charcoal on paper, 40.7 × 55.9 (16 × 22)

Provenance: The artist's sister, Violet Ormond; presented to the British Museum, 1936

Exhibition: Probably London 1926 (259)

Literature: Mount 1969, repr.

Lent by the Trustees of the British Museum

15 *Madame Gautreau* c.*1883–4*

Pencil on paper, 19 × 14.6 (7½ × 5¾)

Inscribed in the artist's hand on the reverse: *A profile / to be returned to London*

Provenance: The artist's sister, Violet Ormond; thence by family descent

Exhibitions: Copley Hall, Boston, 1899 (95), 'Profile'; Tate Gallery 1926, cat. p.8; London 1926 (203)

Literature: *Gazette des Beaux Arts*, xxix (1 June 1884), p.465, repr.; *Studio*, xix (1900), p.107, repr.; repr. Meynell, 1903, 1927; Mount 1969, p.89

Lent by the Ormond Family

These drawings of Madame Gautreau represent some of the thought which lay behind the final portrait (no.13).

Sargent began sittings with Madame Gautreau in the winter of 1882, but work did not proceed with any great success until he went to stay with her and her husband at their country house, Les Chênes Paramé in Brittany, in the summer of 1883. The conditions under which he worked were trying, for the subject had a restless personality, while the artist was frustrated with her 'unpaintable beauty'. A large number of sketches have survived which make it possible to chart the progress of the final composition. Mount suggests that an oil sketch of the subject at a dinner table, with her hand outstretched with a glass of wine

16 *The Misses Vickers*

and with her head seen in profile (formerly Doctor Pozzi, now Isabella Stewart Gardner Museum, Boston), indicates Sargent's first intention of representing her in a seated position. This could be borne out by other seated sketches (notably one in the Metropolitan Museum of Art, New York).

In all of these the figure gives the impression of sensual languidness, the body in an exaggerated twisted motion and the emphasis on her pointed facial features. The seated compositions represented here, in one of which she is reading a book (possibly allowed in order to placate the sitter's temperament), show her in evening dress, with a low *décolletage* and her hair piled up high. The sketch on the right shows her right arm in an apparently characteristic gesture which, together with many other features, was to be repeated in the final version.

The profile head (no.15) may well represent the final sketch before its translation into paint, although there are differences in the *coiffure*. It represents the sharpness of Madame Gautreau's features with an economy of almost Ingres-like precision. It has been suggested that the pose may derive from Titian's *François I* (Louvre), and the many sketches show his obsessive determination to emphasize her profile.

16 *The Misses Vickers 1884*

Oil on canvas, 137.8 × 182.9 (54¼ × 72)

Signed and dated (bottom right): *John S. Sargent 1884*

Provenance: Douglas Vickers; bequeathed to Sheffield City Art Galleries by the Hon Mrs Vickers

Exhibitions: Salon, 1885 (2192); R.A., 1886 (709); Exposition Universelle, Paris, 1900; *Twenty Years of British Art 1890–1910*, Whitechapel, 1910 (536); Tate Gallery 1926, cat. p.14; London 1926 (8), repr. 'Souvenir', p.57; Royal Scottish Academy, 1928; *British Portraits*, R.A., 1955–6 (481); Birmingham 1964 (9); *Victorian Paintings*,

Mappin Art Gallery, Sheffield, 1968 (150);
Bicentenary Exhibition, R.A., 1968 (414);
Masterpieces, Cartwright Hall, Bradford,
1977

Literature: *Athenaeum*, no.3005 (30 May
1885), p.702; *Gaulois-Salon*, no.1022 (30
April 1885), p.2; *Gazette des Beaux Arts*,
XXXII (1885), p.416; *Nouvelle Revue*, XXXIV
(1885), p.609; *Magazine of Art* (1885),
p.514; *Academy* (15 May 1886), p.352;
Athenaeum, no.3059 (12 June 1886), p.786;
Art Journal (1886), p.250; *Graphic* (22 May
1886), p.554; *Pall Mall Gazette* (1 May 1886),
p.4, and (16 August 1886), p.2; *Pall Mall
Pictures 1886* (195); *Spectator* (1 May 1886),
pp.580–1; *Saturday Review*, LIX (8 May 1886),
p.637; *The Times* (22 May 1886), p.8;
Magazine of Art (1899), p.119, repr.;
Studio, XIX (1900), pp.15, 21, repr.;
Scribner's Magazine, XXXIV (1903), p.530;
Roger Fry, *Transformations* (1926), p.127;
Downes 1925, pp.136–8; Charteris 1927,
pp.68–9, 259; *Vernon Lee's Letters*, ed. I.
Cooper Willis (1937), p.171; Mckibbin
1956, p.127; Henry James, *The Painter's Eye*,
ed. J. L. Sweeney (1956), pp.226–7; Mount
1969, pp.97, 118, 454 (8415); Jeremy Maas,
Victorian Painters (1968), plate 223; Ormond
1970, pp.27, 33, 45, 241, plates 37, 42 and
fig.1; Richard Ormond, *Colby Library
Quarterly*, IX (September 1970), p.175

Lent by Sheffield City Art Galleries

The three Vickers sisters were the daughters
of Colonel Thomas Vickers, head of the well-
known Sheffield engineering firm of that
name: Florence (later Mrs W. H. Hamilton
Gordon), Mabel, and Clara (later Mrs C.
W. Parry, secondly Mrs R. W. Skipwith).

Sargent first became acquainted with the
Vickers sisters in Paris, where they were
studying art. He evidently received the
commission to paint their group portrait by
early 1884 for he wrote to Vernon Lee early
in the year: 'Will you be in England next
summer? If so I shall see you there for I am
to paint several portraits in the country and
three ugly young women at Sheffield . . .'
(Colby College, Maine). Sargent had also
become acquainted with another branch of
the Vickers family who lived at Lavington,
near Petworth in Sussex.

Sargent crossed to England on 10 June
1884, probably with a sense of relief after
the hostile reception of *Madame X* (no.13) at
the Salon the previous month. It seems
clear that he did not intend staying longer
than a few months, however, for he lacked

any substantial contacts in order to sustain
a career as a portrait painter. He spent a
few weeks in London meeting other Anglo-
Americans and members of the art establishment, including Mrs Barrington, the future
biographer of Lord Leighton and G. F.
Watts. Shortly afterwards he departed, first
for Sussex to paint *Mrs Albert Vickers*
(private collection), *The Dinner Table at
Night* (no.20) and *Garden Study of the Vickers
Children* (no.21), thence to Sheffield to paint
this portrait.

Stylistically *The Misses Vickers* represents
a development of Sargent's depiction of
figures within an interior. It does not
possess the same compositional debt to
Velazquez as his previous large group,
The Daughters of Edward D. Boit (no.10). It
does, however, follow and refine upon a
number of other interior scenes which show
a predominant interest in darkened rooms,
reflecting objects and a strong sense of tonal
contrasts. It remained an experimental work
in so far as his commissioned work was
concerned, and its unpopularity probably
caused Sargent to abandon such daring
foreshortening and elaborate compositional
techniques. Sargent's later groups depicting
three sisters–*The Wyndham Sisters* (1899;
Metropolitan Museum of Art, New York),
The Hunter Sisters (1902; Tate Gallery,
London) and *The Acheson Sisters* (no.47)–are
in entirely different styles but continue to
explore the possibilities of this theme. The
reception of this picture at the Salon in 1885
was favourable despite the furore of the
preceding year's entry. Vernon Lee arrived
in Paris for a few days *en route* for London
and wrote to her mother on 25 June 1885:
'Yesterday morning he [Sargent] took me to
the Salon & then I lunched with him. His
work of this year is remarkably good; but
unfortunately his principal picture is hung
by the side of Whistler's Lady Archie
Campbell, which beats John into fits. I fear
John is getting rather into a way of painting
people too *tense*. They look as if they were in
a state of crispation de nerfs . . .'

Vernon Lee's comments heralded the
fierce outburst from the English public and
Press when the picture was exhibited at the
Royal Academy the following year. There is
a story that Herkomer threatened to resign
from the Hanging Committee when the
picture was initially refused, but no evidence
for this has come to light. The critics spoke
of its 'cleverness' and 'French' qualities in
disparaging terms. Harry Quilter in the
Spectator wrote of it as 'the *ne plus ultra* of

17 *Violet Sargent*

French painting, or, rather, the French
method as learned by a clever foreigner, in
which everything is sacrificed to technical
considerations . . .'

17 *Violet Sargent* c.*1884*

Water-colour and pencil on paper, 45 × 21.9
(17¾ × 8⅝)

Provenance: The artist's sister, Emily
Sargent; thence by family descent

Exhibitions: Tate Gallery 1926, cat. p.12;
Paris 1963 (30); Birmingham 1964 (55)

Literature: Ormond 1970, p.242, plate 44

Lent by the Ormond Family

This extremely delicate water-colour sketch

of the artist's younger sister was probably painted at the Sargents' house at Nice in early 1884, when the sitter was aged fourteen. She appears in *The Breakfast Table* (Fogg Art Museum, Cambridge, Mass.), probably painted at about the same time.

Sargent's ability to capture a distinctive likeness in water-colour at an early stage in his career is seen brilliantly in this sketch. The somewhat elongated figure is placed centrally and well back within the picture frame. It evokes Sargent's interest in Velazquez, and the subject possesses something of the quality of *The Daughters of Edward D. Boit* (no.10). Sargent's early water-colour technique makes considerable use of thin washes and there is a strong reliance on pencil outlines.

18 *Madame Paul Poirson 1885*

Colour plate III, between pages 8 and 9

Oil on canvas, 152.4 × 86.4 (60 × 34)

Signed and dated (top left): *John S. Sargent 1885*

Provenance: By family descent; purchased by the Detroit Institute of Arts, 1972

Exhibition: Paris 1963 (13)

Literature: Mckibbin 1956, p.116; Mount 1969, pp.91, 448 (851); Ormond 1970, p.33; Larry J. Curry, 'Madame Paul Poirson: an early portrait by Sargent', *Bulletin of the Detroit Institute of Arts*, LI (1972), pp.97–104, repr.

Lent by the Detroit Institute of Arts (Mr and Mrs Richard A. Manoogian, Beatrice Rogers, Gibbs-Williams, and Ralph H. Booth Funds)

Madame Paul Poirson, née Seymourina Cuthbertson, was the natural daughter of the 4th Marquess of Hertford by Madame Oger. She married Paul Poirson, a friend of Gounod and Massenet and brother of the artist Maurice Poirson.

Sargent moved to a studio owned by her husband Paul Poirson, 'where I am better off', at 41 Boulevard Berthier near the Étoile in 1883 (see fig.13), quitting his old one in Rue Notre Dame des Champs. The previous tenant had been Alfred Stevens and it was later taken by Boldini. Photographs of the studio reveal it to have been extremely spacious and fitted out in an advanced style of décor. Vernon Lee gave a splendid description of it in June 1883; 'He has taken

18 *Madame Paul Poirson*

a whole tiny house, so extremely pretty, quite aesthetic and English, with a splendid big studio and pretty garden with roses and all done up with Morris papers and rugs and matting . . . We sat some time in the garden, and drank siphon, John apparently possessing no other food or drink in his house' (*Letters*, ed. I. Cooper Willis, 1937, pp.116–17).

Sargent's new studio, taken on no doubt in anticipation of increasing patronage, was to remain depressingly empty. During 1884 he had completed portraits of *Madame X*, *Edith*, *Lady Playfair*, *Caroline de Bassano* and a number of other sitters. On his return to Paris, however, after a protracted visit to England during the summer and autumn of 1884, very few commissions materialized. By July 1885 Henry James and Vernon Lee had recognized the situation, for she wrote: 'He [Henry James] seems to think that John is in a bad way. Since Madame Gauthereau [*sic*] & one or two other portraits, women are afraid of him lest he should make them too eccentric looking . . .' (Cooper Willis, op.cit. p.177).

The portrait of Madame Paul Poirson is

in total contrast to *Madame X* (no.13). In composition the pose is almost reversed, for here the torso of the figure is slightly in profile while the head is seen in full face with the eyes engaging the spectator in a most direct manner. Curry has rightly pointed out (op.cit.) the naturalness of the pose and the inventiveness of the sitter's conjoined hands with the palms placed downwards. Mount 1969 finds that the long graceful loop of the arms is a new element in Sargent's repertoire. This was later to be repeated in the portrait of *Isabella Stewart Gardner*, but it is significant that the figure of Madame Poirson is seen against a light blue-grey background with none of the trappings so apparent in the early portraits.

Madame Paul Poirson marks the end of Sargent's years in Paris and the end of an identifiable 'French' portrait style. Later he acquired Whistler's old studio at 13 (later renumbered 31) Tite Street, Chelsea, and his preoccupations were to be with impressionism. The romantic but rather unlikely story that this portrait and another of *Suzanne Poirson* (1884; private collection) were painted in lieu of rent cannot be verified beyond family tradition.

Impressionism

Fig.14 Paul Helleu sketching with his wife (see no.31). By courtesy of Mrs P. Howard-Johnston

Fig.15 Javanese dancers; woodcut from *Illustrated London News*, 1889 (see no.34)

The beginning of Sargent's impressionist phase coincides with his departure from Paris and his first years in England. It was an unsettling time for him, when his whole career seemed in jeopardy, and when the opportunity for painting figures and landscapes out-of-doors lay easily to hand. The reverberations from the *Madame X* scandal had an adverse effect on the sources of his patronage in Paris, and by the later part of 1885 he seems to have decided to move to London, though he did not settle permanently till the following year.

A series of pictures painted at Nice around 1883 reveal Sargent's renewed interest in landscape, and they are marked by strong impressionist influence. There are views of houses through trees in which the vibrating effect of light on foliage is conveyed in scratchy, broken brushstrokes and a highly keyed palette.

During his productive summer in England in 1884 Sargent found time to paint the charming garden sketch of the Vickers children, and an intimiste view of the Vickers' dinner-table at night. It was at the Cotswold village of Broadway the following two summers, however, that Sargent's impressionism flowered. Here, surrounded by an intimate circle of artist and writer friends, and unfettered by a large portrait practice, he gave himself up to the boldest *plein-air* experiments. His aim, as Edmund Gosse (no.26) noted was 'to acquire the habit of reproducing precisely whatever met his vision without the slightest previous "arrangement" of detail, the painter's business being, not to pick and choose, but to render the effect before him, whatever it may be . . . His daily plan was to cover the whole of his canvas with a thin coat of colour, so as to make a complete sketch which would dry so rapidly that, next morning, he might paint another study over it. I often could have wept to see the brilliantly fresh and sparkling sketches ruthlessly sacrificed.'

Unfortunately it has not been possible to include Sargent's Broadway masterpiece, *Carnation, Lily, Lily, Rose* (Tate Gallery, London), but here an aesthetic twilight scene is rendered in all its complexity of local colour and tonal ambivalence with astonishing virtuosity. In 1887 Sargent stayed with Monet at Giverny, and it is Monet's influence which is paramount in the series of riverside scenes which Sargent painted at Henley and Calcot on the Thames and at Fladbury on the Avon during the summers of 1887–9. The picture of his sister, *Fishing* (no.30), and *Paul Helleu Sketching with his Wife* (no.31) are brilliant impressionist experiments that quiver with light and colour. Nor is the influence of impressionism confined to out-of-door studies. It permeates his portraits and figure sketches, and gives a new breadth and luminosity to his formal works. Gone is the tight facture and subdued values of his Parisian portraits, though something of the nervous elegance of his French style persists, as in the portrait of *Mrs Harrison* (no.27). The impressionist characteristics of Sargent's portrait style in the 1890s were forged at Broadway and Fladbury.

19 *In a Garden* c.*1883–5*

Colour plate IV, facing page 9

Oil on canvas, 61 × 73.7 (24 × 29)

Provenance: The artist's sister, Violet Ormond; thence by family descent

Exhibition: Washington 1964 (36) (dated c.1884)

Literature: Mount 1969, p.464 (dated 1884 and identified as Nice)

Lent by the Ormond Family

Related stylistically to a group of landscapes painted at Nice around 1883, and a later group painted at Broadway in Worcestershire. The casual choice of viewpoint, the broken brushwork and highly keyed colour point to the strong impact of impressionism on Sargent's style at this time.

The white house seen against a vivid blue sky might at first sight suggest a Mediterranean setting, and there are similar pictures of white houses glimpsed between trees painted in the south of France, for example *Orange Trees, Nice* (private collection), and *House and Garden* (Ormond family). The deep green colour of the meadow, on the other hand, seems more English than French, and there is no lack of comparable Broadway landscapes. Indeed the broad and assured treatment of the work suggests a later rather than an earlier dating. In *Home Fields* (1885; Detroit Institute of Arts), a fence leads the eye into a similar meadow scene with trees painted in the same scratchy and summary style.

The figure in the landscape has not been identified. In her black hat and dark grey cape she strikes a rather discordant note with the brilliant summer scene. She appears to be looking back towards the house, as if suddenly conscious of someone or something behind her. It is typical of Sargent that he should endow his figure with the same naturalism and immediacy as the landscape which she inhabits.

20 *The Dinner Table at Night* (also called *The Glass of Claret*) *1884*

Oil and canvas 51.4 × 68.6 (20¼ × 26¼)

Signed (bottom right): *John S. Sargent*

Provenance: Albert Vickers; by family descent to David Pleydell-Bouverie;

19 *In a Garden*

20 *The Dinner Table at Night*

purchased by the Fine Arts Museum of San Francisco, 1976

Exhibitions: Exposition Internationale de Peinture, Galerie Georges Petit, Rue de Sèze, Paris, 1885 (as 'Verre de Porto'); London 1926 (374); *Sargent and Boldini*, California Palace of the Legion of Honor, San Francisco, 1959 (5); *Three Centuries of American Painting*, California Palace of the Legion of Honor, San Francisco, 1970–1 (43)

Literature: Charteris 1927, pp.68, 115, 282; Mckibbin 1956, p.127; Mount 1969, pp.96, 464 (к841); Ormond 1970, pp.33, 241, plate 38

Lent by the Fine Arts Museums of San Francisco (Atholl McBean Foundation)

The two figures in this painting are Mr and Mrs Albert Vickers of Lavington Rectory, near Petworth in Sussex, with whom Sargent stayed during the summer of 1884. The circumstances of this visit, and Sargent's relationship with the Vickers family, who were important early patrons, are discussed in connection with *The Misses Vickers* (no. 16), and *Garden Study of the Vickers Children* (no.21).

There are a small number of charming interior scenes belonging to the early 1880s which have many features in common. They are generally characterized by a great feeling of spontaneity, unusual viewpoints and informality in the figures. In this painting Sargent's interest is evidently in the effect of the lamplight on the table-cloth of the finished dinner party, and on the figure of Mrs Vickers, whose head is seen in the glow of the dim light. Her face is full of character, while the figure of her husband is seen to the right, with his legs crossed, possibly also enjoying a glass of claret. Important features are the strong contrasts observed under these lighting conditions, and the effect of the reflecting surfaces of the silver and glass objects on the table.

Although Sargent first began to experiment in the effects of painting under natural light in England while staying with the Vickers, he is here painting in an undeniably French idiom, albeit entirely idiosyncratic. The most closely related pictures to this are *The Breakfast Table* (c.1883–4; Fogg Art Museum, Cambridge, Mass.) and *Fête Familiale* (the Besnard family, 1885; Minneapolis Institute of Arts). It foreshadows Sargent's later conversation piece, *An Interior in Venice* (1899; Royal Academy).

21 *Garden Study of the Vickers Children*

21 Garden Study of the Vickers Children c.1884

Oil on canvas, 137.6 × 91.1 (54$\frac{3}{16}$ × 35$\frac{7}{8}$)

Provenance: Albert Vickers; by family descent to David Pleydell-Bouverie; sold by him at Sotheby's Parke-Bernet, New York, 7–8 April 1971 (lot 36); Bressler & Meisen

Exhibitions: London 1926 (580); *Sargent and Boldini*, California Palace of the Legion of Honor, San Francisco, 1959 (4); *Man: Glory, Jest and Riddle*, California Palace of the Legion of Honor, San Francisco, 1964

Literature: *Studio*, XC (1925), repr. p.90; Charteris 1927, pp.68, 73–4 (dated 1884), 283 (dated 1885); Mckibbin 1956, pp.87, 128 (dated 1884); Mount 1969, pp.96, 454 (K859) (dated 1885); Ormond 1970, p.242, plate 45 (dated 1884)

Lent by the Flint Institute of Arts, Michigan (Gift of the Viola E. Bray Trust)

The two figures are Vincent Cartwright and Dorothy (later the Hon Mrs Pleydell-Bouverie), children of Albert Vickers and his wife. Sargent came to their home at Lavington Rectory near Petworth in Sussex in the early summer of 1884 to paint a full-length portrait of *Mrs Albert Vickers* (Vickers family). At the same time he painted the charming sketch of the Vickers dinner table (no.20), and almost certainly the *Garden Study*, though some authorities prefer to date it a year later. From Lavington Sargent moved north to Sheffield to stay with another branch of the Vickers family, owners of the great engineering firm, and there Sargent painted his well-known group of *The Misses Vickers* (no.16).

Sargent's picture of the Vickers children, over-topped by tall lilies in pots, was clearly a trial run for *Carnation, Lily, Lily, Rose* (Tate Gallery, London), which it anticipates closely in mood and idea. Like the later picture, its impressionist treatment was conditioned by aesthetic and poetic considerations. The sentiment and appeal of the picture might be compared to those popular scenes of childhood, like Millais's *Autumn Leaves* (Manchester City Art Gallery) for which the British public had an insatiable appetite. Though the figures and flowers are painted in a bold impressionist manner, and are clearly observed under conditions of natural light, the high viewpoint and the undifferentiated flat colour of the grass serve to accentuate the decorative and aesthetic qualities of the design.

22 *Teresa Gosse*

22 Teresa Gosse 1885

Oil on canvas, 63.5 × 48.3 (25 × 19)

Inscribed and signed (top left): *to Mrs Gosse John S. Sargent*

Provenance: Mrs Edmund Gosse; Sylvia Gosse; Miss Jennifer Gosse, sold Sotheby's, 8 March 1978 (lot 32)

Exhibitions: *Paintings by Edwardian Artists*, Graves Art Gallery, Sheffield, 1954 '(34); Birmingham 1964 (12)

Literature: Mckibbin 1956, p.98; Mount 1969, p.440 (8512)

Lent by Dr and Mrs John J. McDonough

Teresa Gosse, the daughter of the novelist Edmund Gosse (no.26), painted at the Cotswold village of Broadway on her eighth birthday, 14 September 1885. The sitter described the picture herself in a letter of 1948 to David Mckibbin: 'You are quite right about the date when the sketch of me was painted. It was the year when Sargent painted the portrait of my father. We all went to Broadway for the summer holidays. One day when Sargent was painting we children came in from a picnic with bunches of autumn colchicum [meadow saffron]. He was so pleased with the colour of the mauve flowers, my red hair, white dress, that he quickly painted a sketch on canvas over a landscape.'

The warm and autumnal mood of the picture, the touching figure of the innocent young girl in white, relate closely to the theme of Sargent's Broadway masterpiece, *Carnation, Lily, Lily, Rose* (Tate Gallery, London). He painted several such vivid studies of children at this time, including a similar study of a girl in white muslin with an ivy wreath in her hair, sometimes entitled *Guinevere* (listed by Mckibbin, p.99).

23 Flora Priestley c.1885–9

Oil on canvas, 63.5 × 48.3 (25 × 19)

Provenance: The artist's sister, Emily Sargent; thence by family descent

Exhibition: Birmingham 1964 (11)

Literature: Mount 1969, p.449 (8510) (dated 1885); Ormond 1970, p.243, plate 49 (dated c.1885)

Lent by the Ormond Family

Miss Flora Priestley (b.1858) was the daughter of Augusta Le Poer Trench and her first husband, the Reverend William Henry Priestley, who was chaplain of the English church at Nice (see *Tate Gallery Catalogue: Modern British Paintings, Drawings and Sculpture*, II, 1964, pp.600–1, quoting information from Mckibbin and Mount). She may well have met Sargent and his sister when they were children at Nice in the 1860s, but her nephew, R. C. Barton, thought it more likely that she had first met the painter when she was studying art in Paris around 1882. She became a close friend of his and of Emily, and an intimate member of their circle in Chelsea, noted for her striking looks and her unconventional dress. There is no doubt that Sargent was much impressed by her beauty, and she posed to him for a number of portrait studies during the 1880s. There is said to have been a romance between them. According to C. M. Mount ('The English Sketches of J. S. Sargent', *Country Life*, CXXXV, 1964, p.934), Sargent asked Flora Priestley to marry him on several occasions, while according to Ormond family tradition it was he who held back from marriage.

The chronology of Sargent's studies of Flora is difficult to determine. The largest is the threequarter-length in the Tate Gallery, a weird and exotic work that emphasizes the sitter's oriental appearance. This has been dated by most authorities to the summer of 1889, when Flora stayed with Sargent and his sisters at Fladbury Rectory in Worcestershire. Another head-and-shoulders study of her singing by candlelight, and an oil sketch of her and Violet Ormond on a couch (both Ormond family), have also been associated with this visit. An earlier study, called *The Cigarette* or *Lady with Candelabra* is dated 1885. A half-length portrait, which certainly seems to show Flora at a younger age than the others (formerly R. C. Barton), was dated by Mckibbin to 1884 (p.117), but by Mount to 1889 (8914). The portrait exhibited here might have been painted at any point between those two dates, although an earlier dating is perhaps preferred on grounds of style.

The portrait is very thinly painted and it has suffered damage in the past, especially in the blacks. It is altogether more freely and broadly painted than the contemporary portrait of *Violet Sargent* (no.25), in a style that recalls Manet, with the characteristic accent of a flower relieving a colour scheme of greys and blacks. The silhouette of the figure is elegant and attenuated, the face with its strangely arched eyebrows and high cheekbones full of nervous refinement. Fluidity of style is allied here to acute sensibility. A drawing of Flora Priestley and a later water-colour of her also belong to the Ormond family.

24 *Fanny Watts* c.*1885–9* (?)

Water-colour on paper, 33 × 23 (13 × 9)

Provenance: The artist's sister, Violet Ormond; thence by family descent

Exhibitions: London 1926 (532); Paris 1963 (24); Birmingham 1964 (53)

Lent by the Ormond Family

Fanny Watts was one of Sargent's childhood friends. His first contribution to the Salon in 1877 had been a threequarter-length portrait of her (Philadelphia Museum), and he also drew her at St Enogat in 1876 (no.1). In comparison with Fanny's youthful appearance in these early portraits, the water-colour appears to show a considerably older woman. No early water-colour studies of this kind are known, and the style accords much better with the few extant examples of the 1880s. The water-colour of Helleu (no.32) provides a good comparative example. Like this study, the water-colour of Fanny Watts is subdued in colour but full of nervous vitality.

23 *Flora Priestley*

24 *Fanny Watts*

25 *Violet Sargent 1886*

Oil on canvas, 70 × 56 (27½ × 22)

Signed and dated (top left and right):
John S. Sargent 1886

Provenance: The sitter; thence by family
descent

Exhibitions: Falmouth 1962 (2);
Washington 1964 (37)

Literature: Mount 1955, p.431 (8612)

Lent by the Ormond Family

A portrait of the artist's younger sister,
Violet, later Mrs Francis Ormond (1870–
1955), at the age of sixteen, probably
painted at Bournemouth where Sargent's
parents were temporarily living; a portrait
of Dr Sargent of the same date is in the
Sargent-Murray-Gilman House, Gloucester,
Mass. The youngest of the family by thirteen
years, Violet was adored by her brother and
her elder sister, Emily, and all three remained very close to one another throughout their lives. In 1890 she married Francis
Ormond, the son of a Swiss cigar manu-
facturer, and during her early married life
travelled extensively in Europe and North
Africa. Her three eldest children were
largely brought up by their French grand-
mother, while the youngest three were
educated in England, where Violet and her
husband spent part of each year in a house
in Cheyne Walk, London; they had a
second house in Tunisia.

25 *Violet Sargent*

Sargent painted a number of studies of
Violet as a child and as a young girl (see
no.17), including a painting of her aged
five (Ormond family), and a charming
interior scene called *At the Breakfast Table*
(c.1883–4; Fogg Art Museum, Cambridge,
Mass.). She was also the chief model for the
series of impressionist figure studies which he
painted at Calcot and Fladbury during the
summers of 1888 and 1889 (see no.30).
These studies, together with two vivid
profile portraits of 1889 and 1890 (Ormond

family, and Isabella Stewart Gardner
Museum, Boston), are a tribute to her
beauty, her vitality and her warmth of
personality. She did not lack for admirers,
and one of the people who courted her was
the American painter Dennis Bunker.

The picture exhibited here is the least
known but perhaps the most moving of all
Sargent's characterizations of his sister. It is
very simple and subdued. The warm,
translucent flesh tones take on a deeper
resonance from the prevailing greys and

blacks of the dress and background. The mauve flowers in the dress, the matching ribbon in the hair, and the accent of the diamond brooch at the neck, are brilliant impressionist touches in an otherwise restrained treatment. The sitter looks out with a direct, almost challenging expression, but how tender and mysterious is the artist's conception of her. He gives the strong lines of her character, and with it a sense of the power of her beauty, and perhaps of its transience. A very similar portrait of a sensitive young woman, holding a flower, is that of *Mrs Augustus Hememway* (1890; private collection).

26 *Edmund Gosse 1886*

Oil on canvas, 59.8 × 49.5 (23½ × 19½)

Inscribed and signed (along the top): *To Edmund Gosse from his friend John S. Sargent*

Provenance: The sitter; bequeathed to the Brotherton Library by his son, Sir Philip Gosse, 1959

Exhibitions: Either this or the NPG portrait, Royal Society of Portrait Painters, New Gallery, London, 1894 (118); London 1926 (51) (dated 1886 in catalogue), repr. 'Souvenir', p.50; Birmingham 1964 (13)

Literature: E. Gosse, *Collected Poems* (1911), frontis.; *Bookman*, XLIV (June 1913), repr. p.112 (dated February 1886); Charteris 1927, pp.79, 142, 259; E. Charteris, *Life and Letters of Sir Edmund Gosse* (1931), p.202; *Dictionary of National Biography, 1922–1930* (1932), p.355; Mckibbin 1956, p.98 (dated 1885); Mount 1969, p.440 (862) (dated 1886); Ormond 1970, pp.245-6 (under note to plate 59)

Lent by the Brotherton Library, University of Leeds

Edmund Gosse, later Sir Edmund Gosse (1849–1928), the distinguished critic and man of letters. In the course of a long career, Gosse not only held posts in the British Museum, the Board of Trade and the House of Lords Library, but published many volumes of verse, criticism and biography. He was the first writer to introduce the work of Ibsen to the British public, translating two of his plays. He is best remembered now for *Father and Son* (1907), an autobiographical description of his childhood and a powerful portrait of his overbearing father. Gosse was a witty and entertaining conversationalist, and his wide circle of

26 *Edmund Gosse*

friends included many of the most brilliant men of his time. At the period of this portrait Gosse was Clark Lecturer in English Literature at Trinity College, Cambridge.

Sargent apparently first met Gosse in 1885 at Broadway, Worcestershire, where a group of artists and writers formed a happy summer community. Gosse's vivid account of this time was given to Charteris, who published extracts (Charteris 1927, pp.72–80). Gosse recalled Sargent's dissatisfaction with Paris and his discouragement over his lack of patronage, his discerning comments on artists and pictures, his work on *Carnation, Lily, Lily, Rose* (Tate Gallery, London), and his methods of painting: 'He was accustomed to emerge, carrying a large easel, to advance a little way into the open, and then suddenly to plant himself nowhere in particular ... His object was to acquire the habit of reproducing precisely whatever met his vision without the slightest previous "arrangement" of detail ... He was painting, one noon of this radiant August of 1885, in a white-washed farmyard ... As I approached him, Sargent looked at me, gave a convulsive plunge in the air with his brush, and said "Oh! what lovely lilac hair, no one ever saw such beautiful lilac hair!" The blue sky, reflected on my sleek dun locks, which no one had ever thought "beautiful" before, had glazed them with colour, and Sargent, grasping another canvas, painted me as I stood laughing, while he ejaculated at intervals, "Oh! what lovely hair!" The

real colour of the hair was nothing, it existed only in the violet varnish which a single step into the shade would destroy for ever!' Mckibbin 1956, relying on evidence given to him by Gosse's children, Philip and Teresa (no.22), associates the portrait shown here with the 'lilac hair' incident, but early sources all give 1886 as the date, presumably on information provided by Gosse himself. The portrait certainly does not look like an out-of-door study, and the specific date, 'Feb. 1886', mentioned by the *Bookman*, suggests that it was painted in London. Among the Gosse papers in the Brotherton Library, Leeds, are several from Sargent to Gosse, including one of 28 January 1886, declining an invitation. In a letter of 19 November 1886 to W. D. Howells, Gosse apparently refers to this portrait which an acquaintance saw on the walls of his house, and 'recognized it at once as the man he had been dining with at Trinity' (E. Charteris, loc.cit.). The portrait captures Gosse in a reflective mood, very much as the sensitive and imaginative writer, rather than the worldly socialite and man of letters that most people thought him to be. According to the *DNB* (loc.cit.), Gosse was of medium height, quick in movement and rather Scandinavian in colouring. The portrait has suffered quite badly in the past from bituminous cracking, especially in the background.

A second, more conventional portrait of Gosse, showing him full-face in spectacles, belonged to Alfred Parsons, a painter and a member of the Broadway Set, and is now in the National Portrait Gallery. It was evidently painted at much the same period. In 1894 Sargent refused to allow one of these portraits to be reproduced in the *Yellow Book*, probably the one shown here.

27 *Mrs Robert Harrison 1886*

Colour plate V, facing page 16

Oil on canvas, 156.2 × 78.8 (61½ × 31)

Signed and dated (top left and right): *John S. Sargent 1886*

Provenance: By family descent

Exhibitions: R.A., 1886 (78); *British Painting Since Whistler*, National Gallery, London, 1940 (61)

Literature: *Athenaeum*, no.3059 (12 June 1886), p.786; *Art Journal* (1886), p.187; *The Times* (22 May 1886), p.8; *Country Life*, XX

27 *Mrs Robert Harrison*

(1906), p.594; Sir G. Henschel, *Musings of a Musician* (1917), p.331; Downes 1925, p.143; Charteris 1927, pp.259, 260; Mckibbin 1956, p.100; Mount 1969, pp.108, 117, 441 (865); Ormond 1970, p.40

Lent by Miss Philippa Harrison

Helen Harrison (d.1936) was the daughter of a rich Tyneside ship repairer and politician, Eustace Smith. He and his wife entertained on a lavish scale at 52 Princes Gate, and had a wide circle of friends. Mrs Eustace Smith was an ostentatious and flamboyant figure, who had a succession of lovers, among them Sir Charles Dilke. Her daughter Helen was one of ten children, and around 1877 she married Robert Harrison (d.1924), a rich stockbroker, who had a house, Shiplake Court, on the Thames at Henley. At the time when this portrait was painted Helen Harrison was caught up in the divorce scandal which engulfed her sister, Mrs Crawford, and Sir Charles Dilke,

whom Mrs Crawford cited as one of her lovers. In the course of evidence it appeared that Mrs Crawford and Mrs Harrison had carried on various liaisons with lovers whom on occasion they shared in the same bed. The exposure of the scandal must have had a traumatic effect on the Harrisons, but the marriage survived, and in her later years Mrs Harrison was noted for her moral rectitude.

Sargent's introduction to Robert Harrison may have come through his nephew, Peter Harrison (see no.84), a painter and lifelong friend of the artist, whose future wife, Alma Strettell, Sargent had known for some time. Like Sargent, Robert Harrison was passionately interested in music, acting for a time as honorary treasurer of the London Symphony Concerts. The well-known singer and conductor, Sir George Henschel, first met Sargent at Shiplake Court during the summer of 1887, and at once became a friend and admirer, sitting for his own portrait two years later. In his reminiscences Henschel describes the floating studio which Sargent had constructed on a punt and from which he painted daily. A picture of Alma Strettell, entitled *Under the Willows*, was perhaps painted at this time (Shiplake Court sale, 1925).

Sargent's portrait of *Mrs Harrison* belongs to a group of English portraits painted shortly before or soon after his move to London; it is closest in style to one of *Mrs Douglas Dick* (Mrs R. Drummond Wolff collection). These portraits were mostly painted for friends receptive to the artist's advanced style and outlook, and they helped to tide him over a difficult period in his career. Many of the characteristics of his French portraits are still apparent – the taut sense of design, the elegant attenuation of the figure, and the sensitive response to mood and personality. But Sargent's brushwork is also noticeably looser and richer under the influence of impressionism, and his palette altogether more colourful. *Mrs Harrison* appears to be more natural and less stylized than the slightly earlier and very French portrait of *Madame Poirson* (no.18). Her dress, no doubt carefully selected, emphasizes the slimness of her figure, a vertical line dividing the deep red over-garment from the cream dress beneath in a very striking way. The head, though damaged, is a marvellous index to the tense and vulnerable character of this beautiful woman, and it is complimented by the tentative gesture of the hands.

28 *Cecil Harrison*

That a portrait as elegant as this could arouse antagonism is a telling comment on the state of British taste in the 1880s. The *Art Journal* called the colouring and composition 'eccentric', while the *Athenaeum* felt that the 'rawness and crudity of an uncompromising treatment of the features, forms and expression are carried to excess'. *The Times* was more perceptive, writing 'that the painter has really got in this apparent slighting the truth about his sitters, and that no further touches could put more life, or more character, into face or form or accessories.'

Besides the oil, Sargent also executed two sensitive profile drawings of Mrs Harrison: one said to be dated 1888 (but dated to 1886 by Mckibbin, p.101), sold from the Alan Parsons collection, Sotheby's, 21 November 1962 (lot 57); the other dated 1887, sold at Christie's, 4 March 1977 (lot 66).

28 *Cecil Harrison* c.*1888*

Oil on canvas, 172.8×83.6 (68×32⅞)

Signed (top left): *John S. Sargent*

Provenance: Presented to Southampton Art Gallery by the sitter's mother, Mrs Robert Harrison, through the National Art-Collections Fund, 1935

Exhibitions: R.A., 1888 (314); London 1926 (556); Birmingham 1964 (16)

Literature: *Academy*, XXXIII (26 May 1888), p.365; *Art Journal* (1888), p.217; Downes 1925, p.150; Charteris 1927, p.260; Mckibbin 1956, p.100 (dated 1886); Mount 1969, p.431 (8713) (dated 1887); Ormond 1970, p.40

Lent by Southampton Art Gallery

Cecil Harrison (1878–1915) was the eldest son of the wealthy stockbroker, Robert Hichens Camden Harrison, and of his wife, Helen, whom Sargent painted in 1886 (no.27). Cecil, a major in the army, was killed on active service during the First World War. The portrait of him has been variously dated 1886 and 1887. It may have been begun at the same time as the portrait of his mother, which it matches in size if not in scale, but the sitter looks nearer in age to ten than eight. He is dressed in a sailor suit, and stands on a rich fur rug, his thumbs casually hooked in his pockets, in a pose full of nervous elegance. It is a sensitive characterization, and one full of suggestiveness, making one feel that the sitter has experience of life beyond his years. He emerges from a shadowy and atmospheric background into a strong sidelight, which throws his face and hands into sharp relief. It is difficult to appreciate now what a modern note such a portrait would have struck in the 1880s, with its brilliant, unstudied realism and its summary execution. The hands, for example, are blurred and barely finished, and the rug is painted in series of swift, impressionistic strokes. Another such rug, treated as a luxuriant accessory to a tensely posed figure, occurs in the 1884 portrait of R. L. Stevenson (Taft Museum, Cincinnati), and in the contemporary full-length of an American sitter, Mrs Elliot Shepard (1888; private collection, USA).

Reaction to the portrait at the Royal Academy was mixed, and it received much less attention than Sargent's two other contributions, *Mrs Marquand* and *Mrs Boit*. The *Art Journal* called it 'One of the fine

29 *Dorothy Barnard*

portraits of the year, the picture is remarkable for the brilliance and purity of the flesh colour and for the truth with which the navy-blue costume has been represented'. In the *Academy* Claude Phillips criticized the work as 'almost conventional in treatment' while admitting its 'intense vitality'.

29 *Dorothy Barnard 1889*

Oil on canvas, 70.5 × 39.4 (27¾ × 15½)

Provenance: Bequeathed to the Fitzwilliam Museum by the sitter, 1949

Exhibitions: Tate Gallery 1926, cat. p.3; London 1926 (595); *A Whistler and 20th Century Oils*, National Gallery, London, 1941 (21); Birmingham 1964 (19)

Literature: Charteris 1927, p.261; Mckibbin 1956, p.83 (dated Fladbury 1887, the last numeral clearly a mistake); Mount 1969, p.431 (891); J. W. Goodison, *Fitzwilliam Museum Catalogue of Paintings: III, British School* (1977), pp.216–17

Lent by the Syndics of the Fitzwilliam Museum, Cambridge

Dorothy Barnard (1878–1949) was the daughter of the artist and illustrator Frederick Barnard, and of his wife Alice Faraday. Frederick Barnard died young, but Mrs Barnard and her two daughters remained warmly attached to the Sargent and Ormond families. They moved in the same circles in London, and often spent their holidays together in the Alps (see fig. 10). This charming out-of-doors sketch of Dorothy was painted at Fladbury, where Sargent had taken the rectory for the summer, entertaining his friends and painting a succession of riverside scenes (see no.31). He also delighted in seizing on his companions to dash down a sketch of them in some attitude or light effect that suddenly caught his fancy. He had done the same at Broadway, and in the relaxed atmosphere of Fladbury he was no less productive. His sister Violet, the Barnard girls, Flora Priestley, Kit Anstruther-Thompson, Mrs L. A. Harrison, and the Helleus, all figure in surviving portrait studies, or what might in some cases more properly be called figure arrangements.

In this picture Sargent seems less concerned with the specific character of his sitter than with the idea of a pretty young girl. She is dressed in soft and summery colours, and strikingly posed in profile against a dark doorway. No doubt it was the sudden sight of Dorothy leaning against a doorpost with her hands behind her back that first started Sargent off, and the immediacy of his impression remains. But what is remarkable about the study is the way in which his vision of her has been translated into a strong pictorial design, reminiscent in its use of a profile pose of *Madame Gautreau* (no.13). Like *Carnation, Lily, Lily, Rose* (Tate Gallery, London), for which Dorothy had posed three years earlier, the technique may be impressionistic, but the mood is tender and aesthetic.

30 *Fishing 1889*

Oil on canvas, 185 × 98 (72¾ × 38½)

Provenance: Presented to the Tate Gallery by Miss Emily Sargent, in memory of her brother, through the National Art-Collections Fund, 1929

Exhibitions: London 1926 (403), repr. 'Souvenir', p.58; Tate Gallery 1926, cat. p.10; Birmingham 1964 (18)

Literature: Charteris 1927, pp.99, 283;

N.A.-C.F. Report 1929 (1930), p.44; National Gallery Millbank [Tate Gallery] Review of the Acquisitions 1927–29 (1930), frontis.; Mckibbin 1956, p.113; Tate Gallery Catalogue: The Modern British Paintings, Drawings and Sculpture, II (1964), p.601; C. M. Mount, 'The English Sketches of J. S. Sargent', Country Life, CXXXV (1964), p.934, repr. p.931; Mount 1969, p.467 (K899); Ormond 1970, p.245, under note to plate 56

Lent by the Tate Gallery
Exhibited London only

The artist's younger sister, Violet (see nos. 17 and 25), painted at Fladbury in Worcestershire. This is the largest and most ambitious of the *plein-air* subjects which Sargent painted during the summer. It was almost certainly intended as an exhibition piece, and, despite its damaged and unfinished state, it remains an impressive record of Sargent's attempt to reconcile formal figure painting with the tenets of impressionism. The extensive linear cracking of the paint suggests that the canvas was rolled at some time, and the paint on the foldovers may indicate that the composition was once larger. The fishing rod itself is barely indicated and, the sitter's right hand looks very strange as a result.

The figure is conceived in monumental terms, the profile pose of the head, with its appealing toque hat, suggesting analogies with *Madame X* (no.13). Violet's delicately pink complexion glows with health and vitality. A preliminary oil sketch for the picture (72.5 × 53.3; Ormond family) shows the figure much more casually posed, with far more surrounding space and a view of the far river-bank (this is just suggested in the large version in the dark green reflections top right). In the big picture the accidental effects of light and brushwork are carefully controlled. The broken folds of the muslin dress are smoothed away, the reflections on the water formalized into broad, aesthetic patterns. The high and unusual viewpoint has the effect of flattening the space and enhancing the decorative effect of the figure in relationship to the landscape. But the feeling of reflected light, the blurred treatment of the bank in the foreground, and the luminous colour underline the impressionist sources of Sargent's vision. The white dress, for example, is rendered almost entirely in blues and greys and grey-blues as it picks up the light from the water, and the colour of the river itself ranges from deep purple to the palest blue.

30 *Fishing*

At Calcot and Fladbury Sargent painted a whole series of riverside scenes in which his sister and his friends appear (see no.31). An immediate precursor of *Fishing* was the *Morning Walk* (Ormond family), a brilliant Monetesque study of Violet painted at Calcot, and she appears in the same toque hat in several Fladbury sketches, including *Two Girls with Parasols* (Metropolitan Museum of Art, New York), *The Lowest Terrace, Fladbury* (Ormond family), and *Autumn on the River* (Danielson collection). In comparison with these river scenes *Fishing* is more consciously designed and more deliberately aesthetic in its intentions.

31 *Paul Helleu Sketching with his Wife 1889*

Oil on canvas, 66 × 81.3 (26 × 32)

Signed (bottom right): *John S. Sargent*

Provenance: Sold by Helleu to Brooklyn Museum, 1920

Exhibitions: New English Art Club, winter 1892 (71); Pennsylvania Academy, Philadelphia, 1922 (253); New York 1926 (21); *Sargent, Whistler and Mary Cassatt*, Art Institute of Chicago and Metropolitan Museum of Art, New York, 1954 (57); Washington 1964 (43)

Literature: *Figaro Illustré* (September 1901), repr. in colour; *Scribner's Magazine*, XXXIV (1903), p.532; *L'Art et Les Artistes* (December 1904), repr. p.379; repr. Meynell 1903, 1927; Downes 1925, pp.154–5; Charteris 1927, pp.133, 261; Mckibbin 1956, p.101; C. M. Mount, 'The English Sketches of J. S. Sargent', *Country Life*, CXXXV (1964), p.934, repr.; D. Hoopes, 'John S. Sargent and the Worcestershire Interlude', *Brooklyn Museum Annual*, VII (1966), pp.74–89, repr. in colour; Mount 1969, pp.156, 466 (K8910); Ormond 1970, pp.42, 245, col. plate 1 and plate 57

Lent by The Brooklyn Museum

Paul César Helleu (1856–1927), the French painter and etcher, with his wife, Alice Louise Guérin, whom he had married in 1886 when she was sixteen. Helleu had been a close friend of Sargent since they were both students at Carolus-Duran's studio in the late 1870s. In the 1890s Sargent did a great deal to promote his friend's career in England, pushing his work at exhibitions and finding him patrons. Helleu was a handsome and elegant figure, a friend of Proust and other writers, an entertaining conversationalist and a great womanizer. There are numerous portraits and sketches of him by Sargent, several done at Fladbury in Worcestershire, where Helleu brought his young wife to stay for a painting holiday during the summer of 1889.

The Helleus feature in a number of the riverside scenes that Sargent painted at Fladbury. They appear casually sprawled in a punt and canoe in the *Boating Party* (Metcalf collection), a vivid, unstudied sketch in which the landscape predominates. By comparison the figures in this picture are carefully characterized, and under the brilliant impressionist surface freedom is a taut sense of design. As with *Fishing* (no. 30) there is little sense of spatial recession, and the figures are seen abruptly against an almost flat backcloth of grass and water. The red canoe establishes the dominant diagonal line of the composition, echoed in the arrangement of the figures. Helleu is all nervous energy, bony knees wide apart, long

31 *Paul Helleu Sketching with his Wife*

32 *Paul Helleu Seated before the Fire*

33 *Vernon Lee*

nervous fingers dabbing at the canvas, head down in concentration. By contrast his beautiful wife, in a white bonnet matching his boater, appears languorous, listless and moody, a picture of the bored wife dutifully attending her husband.

That Sargent took considerable pains with the picture can be shown by the many related sketches of Madame Helleu which he drew at the time, some in a sketchbook in the Fogg Art Museum (no.1937.7.16), others belonging to Helleu's daughter (exhibited Paris 1963, 33–38). There is also a photograph of the couple obviously taken while they were sitting for the picture, and perhaps used by the artist as a record of the pose (fig. 14). The picture must have taken several days to complete, and may well have been worked on in the studio. The result is a skilful mood piece, with vividly conceived figures placed in a glowing landscape. The painting of the grasses and reeds is an impressionistic *tour de force*. One is reminded of *Carnation, Lily, Lily, Rose* (Tate Gallery, London), where the foreground vegetation is painted in long slashing strokes that convey the vibrations of light with astonishing immediacy.

32 *Paul Helleu Seated before the Fire 1889* (?)

Water-colour on paper, 23.5 × 37.3 (9¼ × 14⅝)

Provenance: The artist's sister, Violet Ormond; thence by family descent

Exhibitions: Paris 1963 (32); Birmingham 1964 (56)

Lent by the Ormond Family

Perhaps painted at Fladbury on the same occasion as the picture of Helleu sketching with his wife (no.31). The scene is brilliantly captured and in the most succinct way: the firelight, with its flickering shadows; the long black figure stretched out, one hand with a cigarette eloquently raised; the face animated and expressive. One is strongly reminded of Sargent's oil portrait of R. L. Stevenson (Taft Museum, Cincinnati), a similarly lean figure in a chair, legs crossed, cigarette in hand, face intensely alight.

33 *Vernon Lee 1889*

Pencil on paper, 33.7 × 23 (13¼ × 9)

Inscribed, signed and dated (bottom right): *to Miss Anstruther Thomson. Aug. 1889 / John S. Sargent*

Provenance: Miss Clementina (Kit) Anstruther-Thomson; bequeathed by her to Vernon Lee, 1921; bequeathed to the Ashmolean Museum by her friend, Miss Mabel Price, 1939

Exhibitions: Copley Hall, Boston, 1899 (106); *British Portraits*, R.A., winter, 1956–7 (747), repr. 'Souvenir', p.57; Birmingham 1964 (89); *English Portraits*, National Museum of Western Art, Tokyo, 1975 (149), repr.

Literature: repr. *International Studio*, x (1900); Downes 1925, p.295; *Vernon Lee's Letters*, ed. I. Cooper-Willis (1937), p.313, frontis.; G. Reynolds, *Nineteenth Century Drawings 1859–1900* (1949), plate 45; Mckibbin 1956, p.114; P. Gunn, *Vernon Lee* (1964), frontis.; Mount 1969, p.156; Ormond 1970, p.246, plate 60

Lent by the Visitors of the Ashmolean Museum, Oxford

Vernon Lee, the literary pseudonym of the novelist, essayist and critic Violet Paget (1856–1935). She and Sargent had been intimate friends since their childhood in Nice, and the shared experience of that time remained a lifelong bond between them; much of their surviving early correspondence has been published in the *Colby Library Quarterly*, ix, 1970, pp.154–78. In

Colour plate **IX**
The Hon Victoria Stanley 1899 (no.43)

Colour plate X *The Acheson Sisters 1902* (no.47)

1881 Sargent painted a brilliant oil sketch of Vernon Lee (Tate Gallery, London), and her letters of this time provide invaluable details of his life in Paris and London. As time went on the intimacy of their relationship cooled, but they remained faithful old friends, and continued to meet regularly. Sargent was often irritated by Vernon Lee's intellectual pugnacity, her high-flown aesthetic and psychological theories, while she on her side could not penetrate his reserve. Her important essay on Sargent was appended to Charteris's biography.

Vernon Lee came to Fladbury Rectory as a guest of Sargent with her friend and collaborator Kit Anstruther-Thomson, with whom she was deeply involved emotionally. She arrived on 27 July and described the 'big old-fashioned house, with lawn going down to the Avon: beautiful & so fresh and peaceful'. She departed a month later, regretting its 'kind, kind people', leaving her friend behind (a source of some jealousy), who was being painted by Sargent and taking lessons from him. In September Vernon Lee sent a facsimile of this drawing to her friend Mary Robinson, so she obviously approved of it. The drawing, showing Vernon Lee in bow-tie and boater, certainly captures her sharp and idiosyncratic personality in a telling way. In comparison with Sargent's later charcoals, the style of draughtsmanship is delicate and precise.

34 *Javanese Dancer 1889*

Oil on canvas, 174×76.2 ($68\frac{1}{2} \times 30$)

Provenance: The artist's sister, Violet Ormond; thence by family descent

Exhibitions: London 1926 (59), repr. 'Souvenir', p.54; Washington 1964 (42)

Literature: Downes 1925, p.155; Charteris pp.102, 284; Mount 1969, pp.151, 153, 467 (K8914); Ormond 1970, pp.43, 247, plate 64

Lent by Ian Hugo Hughes
Exhibited London and Detroit only

In the spring of 1889 Sargent visited the Exposition Universelle in Paris to which he had contributed a number of pictures. One of the attractions at the exhibition was a troupe of Javanese dancing girls who performed in the specially constructed Java village. The *Illustrated London News* described their performance, and included a woodcut (XCV, 6 July, 1889, pp.17–20; fig.15):

34 *Javanese Dancer*

'The male dancer and one of the females, the "Bong-geng", are performers of inferior rank, who are qualified only to display the common kind of popular entertainment. But four of these young ladies, whose names are Sarrkiem, Thamina, Soukia, and Ouakiham, the youngest of whom is twelve years of age, and the eldest sixteen, are of the highest class in their profession, the Order of the "Tandkak"; they are of good birth, have been carefully educated in a sort of nunnery, and are trained, like the famous "Bayaderes" of ancient India, to assist in certain mystical rites of temple worship . . . Their dresses, made of the richest embroidered silks and velvets, with massive golden ornaments, necklaces, bracelets, and jewelled head-dresses, are carefully regulated, and seem to have been copied from the costumes of sacred figures in the antique bas-reliefs that still exist among the Khmer ruins of temples in Cambodia . . . Their performance, of which we give an illustration, is accompanied by the orchestral music of the "Gamelang"; and though it may seem dull and monotonous – consisting of slow, gliding movements, wavings of the arms, and waftings of the scarf, with a pantomime understood to be symbolical of some mythological legend of the gods and heroes – it has a rather impressive effect'.

Sargent painted no less than three full-length studies of the dancers, one of which he sent to the New English Art Club in 1891 (probably the second picture belonging to the Ormond family, the third is in a private collection in the USA). He also painted a picture of one of the dancers at her toilet (private collection), and a narrower version of the study shown here for a screen designed by Alma-Tadema (now Gulbenkian Foundation). In a letter of 23 July 1889 to Isabella Stewart Gardner (Fenway Court), Sargent's old friend, Ralph Curtis, wrote to say that he had left Sargent behind in Paris, finishing two fine portraits and five big studies of Java dancing girls at the Exposition. A sketchbook in the Metropolitan Museum of Art, New York, shows studies of the girls dancing, details of head-dresses, arms and so forth, and an attempted notation of the music. There are also one or two surviving water-colours of the dancers that appear to record actual performances (one repr. Ormond 1970, fig.20). It seems inconceivable that Sargent could have painted his pictures without sittings, but how and where they were arranged is not

known. The dancers had been brought over by a Dutchman, Cores de Bries, and it is possible that he made special arrangements for sittings; Sargent is unlikely to have been the only artist keen to paint them.

In spite of their large scale, Sargent's studies of the Javanese dancers are painted thinly and translucently, with visible pentimenti; alternative positions for the dancer's left hand are clearly shown in this picture. A few months before painting the dancers, Sargent had finished a portrait of *Ellen Terry as Lady Macbeth* (Tate Gallery, London), combining a likeness of the actress with a dramatic role, as he was later to do with *Carmencita* (no.35). Unlike Ellen Terry, the Javanese dancers are not self-conscious theatrical personalities, but stylized figures realized in the rhythm of their dance. Their classic elegance of pose and movement, their attenuated gestures, and their exotic accoutrements (the girl in this study has a dagger in her waistband), appealed to Sargent's love of the bizarre, and satisfied his formal preoccupations. The loose, improvized handling and the suffused colour of these studies corresponds to the artist's *plein-air* studies, like the riverside pictures of his sister (see no.30), where the decorative intention is similar.

35 *La Carmencita* 1890

Oil on canvas, 228 × 138.4 (90 × 54½)
Signed (top left): *John S. Sargent*

Provenance: Bought from the artist by the Musée du Luxembourg, 1892

Exhibitions: Society of American Artists, New York, 1890; R.A., 1891 (544); Société Nationale des Beaux Arts, Paris, 1892; American Art, Paris 1919; London 1926 (277), repr. 'Souvenir', p.1; Paris 1963 (18); Washington 1964 (52); *Europa 1900*, Ostend, 1964 (60)

Literature: *Academy*, XXIX (16 May 1891), p.471; *Art Journal* (1891), p.198; *Athenaeum*, no.3314 (2 May 1891), p.577; *Black and White*, I (1891), p.461; *Graphic*, XL (23 May 1891), p.540; *Illustrated London News*, XC (2 May 1891), p.573; *Magazine of Art* (1891), p.254; *Saturday Review*, LXXI (1891), p.621; *Spectator* (2 May 1891), p.625; *The Times* (2 May 1891), p.14; *Studio*, XIX (1900), pp.21, 115, repr.; *Scribner's Magazine*, XXXIV (1903), pp.528, 532, and LXXV (1924), pp.345–6; repr. Meynell 1903, 1927; *Letters of George Meredith*, II (1912),

p.455; Downes 1925, pp.31–2, 160–1, repr.; J.–E. Blanche, 'Un Grand Americain', *Revue de Paris*, XXX (1926), p.560; Charteris 1927, pp.109–13, 116, 263; G. P. Jacomb Hood, *With Brush and Pencil* (1925), p.313; W. Graham Robertson, *Time Was* (1931), pp.244–6; T. Martin Wood, *Sargent: Masterpieces in Colour* (undated), pp.25–6, repr.; Mount 1969, pp.150, 164–74, 204–5, 433 (9019); Ormond 1970, pp.43, 246–7, plate 63
Lent by the Musée du Louvre

La Carmencita was a Spanish dancer who enjoyed a considerable vogue in England and America during the 1890s. Sargent may have encountered her for the first time at the Exposition Universelle in Paris in 1889.

While Sargent was in New York early in 1890 Carmencita gave a private performance at a party given by his old friend from Paris, Carroll Beckwith, on the occasion of his wife's birthday. It was soon after this that Carmencita consented to pose for him, but, like *Madame X* (no.13), the portrait was not commissioned by the sitter. Her character and dark sensuality are certainly in keeping with many of Sargent's preferred types, ranging from the *Head of Ana-Capri Girl* (1878; no.3) to *Ena and Betty Wertheimer* (1901; no.46). It is significant that Sargent's predilection for actresses (or soi-disant actresses) is at its strongest at this time, and his sitters include *Isabella Stewart Gardner* (1888; Isabella Stewart Gardner Museum, Boston), *Ellen Terry as Lady Macbeth* (1889; Tate Gallery, London), the latter in a highly dramatic pose. Later he was to begin a portrait of *Eleonora Duse* (1893; no. 38), and W. Graham Robertson (op.cit.) related how he nearly came to portray Sarah Bernhardt. Her rival, Ada Rehan, was painted by Sargent in 1894–5.

The sense of theatre in this portrait is immediate as the figure steps boldly out of the darkened background into the footlights, with her right foot forward and one hand on her hip. The flaunting nature of the pose is emphasized again in the head thrown back in a defiant gesture. This is in total contrast to the demure qualities of *Lady Agnew* (1893; no.37). The bejewelled short dress of the dancer entirely captures the tinselled effects for which she was renowned. Sargent himself said that he had spent a fortune 'on bracelets and things' in order to placate her wild temperament and to keep her attention. The brushwork of the dress is almost the culmination of the bravura style of this period, and in later years Sargent regretted that he was represented at the Luxembourg by this work, saying: 'After all, it is little more than a sketch' (Charteris 1927, p.113).

The conditions under which the painting was executed could scarcely have been less propitious, as the dancer was performing every night, and Sargent had a large number of commissions on hand. It is not entirely clear how he hoped to dispose of the picture, but significantly he arranged a party at William Merritt Chase's New York studio for Mrs Gardner to see the dancer perform and for her to see the picture which was still unfinished. However, it was not taken up by the owner of *El Jaleo*, and it returned to England later in the summer with the artist. When it was exhibited at the Royal Academy the following year it was his first real unqualified success, the *Art Journal* proclaiming it: '. . . the picture of the year . . . with something of that halo of decay which gives a lurid fascination to the creations of Baudelaire . . .'.

Sargent's admiration for Carmencita was more for her ability as a singer than as a dancer. W. Graham Robertson remembered a party given by Sargent a few years later at which she danced in a short dress: 'She postured and paced, she ogled, she flashed her eyes and her teeth, she was industriously Spanish in the Parisian and American manner . . . Later she reappeared in a dress of dead white, falling to her feet, with a long, heavy train; she wore no jewels, only one dark red rose behind the ear. And she sang the wild, crooning "Palona", and as she sang she circled with splendid arm movements, the feet hardly stirring, the white train sweeping and swinging round her . . .' (op.cit. pp.245–6).

There are several drawings of Carmencita's head (Musée d'Art Moderne, Paris, Museum of Fine Arts, Boston, Fogg Art Museum, Cambridge, Mass.), and an oil sketch in the Ormond family collection. A photograph of her is reproduced in Mount 1969, between pages 144 and 145. W. M. Chase also painted Carmencita in deliberate rivalry to Sargent (Ormond 1970, p.247).

35 *La Carmencita*

36 *Joseph Jefferson 1890*

Oil on canvas, 47×38 ($18\frac{1}{2} \times 15$)

Signed (top right): *J.S.S.*

Provenance: The artist; his sister, Violet Ormond; thence by family descent

Exhibitions: Museum of Fine Arts, Boston, 1890; New English Art Club, summer 1893 (49); Copley Hall, Boston, 1899 (57); Carfax Gallery, London, 1903; San Francisco, 1915; Corcoran Gallery, Washington, 1916–17; St Botolph Club, Boston, 1922; Grand Central Galleries, New York, 1924 (17); New York 1926 (23); Washington 1964 (17)

Literature: repr. Meynell 1903, 1927; Downes 1925, p.157; Charteris 1927, p.262; Mckibbin 1956, p.103; Mount 1969, pp.180, 443 (9017); Ormond 1970, pp.43, 249, plate 74

Lent by Ian Hugo Hughes

Joseph Jefferson (1829–1905), the famous American comic actor. According to the *Dictionary of American Biography*, it was 'because of his whimsical, kindly, honest, and sparkling personality, as well as his art' that 'he became one of the best-loved figures in American life.' In 1889 Sargent had painted *Ellen Terry as Lady Macbeth* (Tate Gallery, London), and he had also experimented with one or two Shakespearian subjects. The theatre was very much in his mind, and during his tour of the United States in 1890 he painted portraits of three distinguished American actors for the Players Club in New York: Lawrence Barrett, Edwin Booth and Joseph Jefferson. Only Jefferson is shown in character, as Dr Pangloss in George Colman's *The Heir at Law*, a part for which he was famous. While painting this larger portrait, Sargent also executed for his own pleasure the vivid sketch shown here. There is an explosive dynamism to the sketch, the force of the brushstrokes summoning up the humorous, almost puckish character of the old actor. The face emerges from a dark background with an intense, almost startled expression, as if unexpectedly caught in a beam of strong light. The sketch, which remained with the artist, was one of which he must have felt proud, because he sent it to represent his work in a series of early exhibitions.

36 *Joseph Jefferson*

The Great London Years

Fig.16 Painting Mrs Fiske Warren and her daughter, Gothic Room at Fenway Court, Boston, 1903

Sargent's success in England had been established by the purchase of *Carnation, Lily, Lily, Rose* by the Chantrey Bequest in 1887, and was followed up by the enthusiastic response to *La Carmencita* (no.35) in 1891. Throughout the nineteenth century it was the pronouncements of the large army of art journalists at the annual summer exhibition of contemporary art at the Royal Academy which could make or break the career of an aspiring artist. Sargent had received a full measure of criticism during the early part of his career, but it was the unequivocal success of *Lady Agnew* (no.37) in 1893 which established him as *the* portrait painter of his day. The later nineteenth century had not found a presiding genius to follow in the path of Lawrence, and had relied on the rather pedestrian output of Millais, Holl, Herkomer and Ouless. The achievements of G. F. Watts and Whistler in this field lay outside the Royal Academy tradition, and the establishment art world was in need of an artist to fulfil the supremely important function of reinstating portrait painting on the high pedestal established by Reynolds. It should also be noted that the Victorian passion for subject pictures was declining by the end of the century.

During the 1890s Sargent's style became more powerful and expressive. His technique is characterized by a brilliant array of forceful brushstrokes, indicating every feature, plane and tonal relationship, which often only make sense when seen from the correct distance. His easel would be placed next to his sitter, so that when he walked back he could view both in the same light. Many sitters remembered the way that he would charge at the canvas with his brush from a considerable distance, uttering strange incomprehensible noises, and then retire to consider the result. He might first indicate the outline of a figure with some charcoal lines, creating a general tone over the background of a head to define its mass. The features would then be modelled in large planes, as though the head were an apple, seeking to define the mass through the middle tones, and nothing would be corrected or altered without repainting the entire understructure. The result is an extraordinary lucidity and fluency, even in the most formal pictures. He always painted with a loaded brush, using little or no medium, explaining to a student, 'The thicker you paint, the more your colour flows'.

To his contemporaries Sargent's portraits were said to represent much more than merely the intense presence of living individuals. He was said to possess the gift of profound insight into human character and often to bring out the worst characteristics of his subjects. However, this is probably more an example of the late nineteenth century's enjoyment of making a story out of any work of art than of a conscious attempt by Sargent: indeed, he often declined to become closely acquainted with his sitter in advance of a commission. Nevertheless there is no denying the extreme intensity of some of his male portraits, for example *Coventry Patmore* (no.39).

Many of Sargent's portraits follow certain formulae. The pose of *Lady Agnew* (no.37) is repeated with variations for a number of years, and the flamboyant *Mrs Carl Meyer and her Children* (no.41) derives from *Mrs Hugh Hammersley*. Their originality is undeniable, but with the passage of time their repetition (often requested by the sitter) inevitably became wearying. Around 1900 Sargent's inventiveness was probably at its height, and the enormous *Wyndham Sisters* was perhaps the greatest popular success of his career.

Until 1900 most of Sargent's sitters had been drawn from the Edwardian plutocracy. For the few remaining years of his professional career it was the aristocracy who were his main patrons, and there is a significant change in his style. His portraits were destined for their enormous houses in London and the country, often containing portraits by Van Dyck, Reynolds, Gainsborough and Lawrence, and Sargent's work had to complement these giants of the past. His portraits become more formal, with pillars and columns towering behind his subjects, reaching a climax in the monumental *Marlborough Family*. His debt to the eighteenth-century masters is never mere plagiarism, and with Reynolds in particular he reinterprets the essence while retaining his own technique and panache. Often his sitters failed to excite his imagination, but there is no 'falling off', particularly with those with a pronounced character or sensitivity. Sargent's portraits at this time coincided with a revival of interest in eighteenth-century neo-classical fine and applied arts.

Sargent never attempted to formulate his own school of painting and never employed studio assistants for his prodigious output. His influence was perhaps limited but can be seen in the work of a number of artists, particularly Orpen, Lavery, Furse, Shannon and Brough. Inevitably Sargent became detached from avant-garde tendencies, but he was always esteemed by the younger generation, although, in the words of William Rothenstein, 'he, in spite of his great gifts, remained outside the charmed circle'. It was the French sculptor Auguste Rodin who paid him the most significant compliment by calling him 'the Van Dyck of our times'.

Fig.17 Coventry Patmore (see no.39) c.1894. National Portrait Gallery, London

Fig.18 (*right*) The Duchess of Portland (see no.48) at the Devonshire House Fancy Dress Ball, by Miss A. Hughes, 1897. National Portrait Gallery, London

Fig.19 (*far right*) A. J. Balfour (see no.51), by Sir Benjamin Stone, 1899. National Portrait Gallery, London

37 *Lady Agnew* c.*1892–3*

Cover

Oil on canvas, 125.7 × 100.3 (49½ × 39½)

Signed (top left): *John S. Sargent*

Provenance: Sir Andrew Agnew, Bt; purchased by the National Galleries of Scotland from the Cowan Smith Bequest, 1925

Exhibitions: R.A., 1893 (30); Copley Hall, Boston, 1899 (1); International Exhibition, Carnegie Institute, Pittsburgh, 1924; London 1926 (25)

Literature: *Academy*, LXX (29 April 1893), p.573; *Art Journal* (1893), pp.242–3; *Athenaeum*, no.3423 (3 June 1893), p.704; *Magazine of Art* (1893), p.258; *Black and White*, V (6 May 1893), p.536; *Spectator*, LXX (29 April 1893), p.573; *Saturday Review*, LXXV (1893), p.487; *The Times* (29 April 1893), p.13; *Illustrated London News*, CII (29 April 1893), p.514; *Studio*, XIX (1900), p.21; *Scribner's Magazine*, XXXIV (1903), p.529, and LXXV (1925), p.348; repr. Meynell 1903, 1927; Downes 1925, pp.36, 170–1; Charteris 1927, pp.136, 264; *Vernon Lee's Letters*, ed. I. Cooper Willis (1937), p.352; *Studio*, CXXX (October 1945), p.104, repr.; Mckibbin 1956, p.81; Mount 1969, p.430 (931); Ormond 1970, pp.46, 51, 54, 247, plates 67, 69; R. Gibson, *British Portraits* (1970), repr.

Lent by the National Galleries of Scotland

Lady Agnew, née Gertrude Vernon, was the wife of Sir Andrew Agnew of Lochnaw. Sargent met her through the blue-stocking Helen Dunham, whom he had painted in 1892.

The British public continued to delay their acceptance of Sargent's abilities as a portrait painter, despite his successes at the Royal Academy and the New Gallery with *Carnation, Lily, Lily, Rose* (1887), *La Carmencita* (1891), and *Ellen Terry as Lady Macbeth* (1889). W. Graham Robertson knew Sargent in the early 1890s and wrote that although he was famous, Sargent still lacked a large clientèle: ' "It is positively dangerous to sit to Sargent. It's taking your face in your hands" said a timid aspirant; and many stood shivering on the brink waiting for more adventurous spirits to take the plunge.' (*Time Was*, 1931, p.233.) The artist's main preoccupations at this time were in gathering material for the Boston Public Library, and his portraits were

37 *Lady Agnew*

mainly of Americans as a result of his visit there in 1890.

In 1893 two portraits finally established Sargent's English career: *Mrs Hugh Hammersley* (private collection), exhibited at the New Gallery, was an exercise in his flamboyant style with the well-known social figure posed at the edge of a sofa in an attitude of great vivaciousness. In contrast, *Lady Agnew*, shown at the Royal Academy, reveals more modest and demure qualities which established a social prestige both for the sitter and the artist. While the exhibition was still open Vernon Lee wrote to her mother (16 July 1893): 'There is a talk of my going early in September with Helen Dunham to her friend Lady Agnew, a very pretty woman whom John Sargent has just made into a society celebrity by a very ravishing portrait.' Seated on a bergère with one arm in her lap, Lady Agnew engages the spectator with a beguiling directness. The tonality of the painting is of pastel colours, ranging from the creams of her dress, the mauve sash and the pale blue Japanese silks – all in a naturally harmonious scheme. The figure is lit from the left and the head shows Sargent's brilliance in modelling by tonal values. The free treatment of the paint adds to the sensation of luxurious abandonment implicit in the design.

Although badly hung, the portrait created a sensation at the Academy, particularly when compared with the work of other British portraitists. The *Magazine of Art* described it as 'a work so subtle and refined, so exquisite in colour, so dignified in repose and grace, so individual in its manner, so masterful in technique, that it will be held by many to be the finest canvas ever put forth by Mr Sargent and one of the best portraits of the day.' *The Times* described it as ' . . . a masterpiece . . . those who can abstract it from its surroundings will not fail to see in it not only a triumph of *technique* but the finest example of portraiture in the literal sense of the word, that has been seen here for a long while. . . . If he will only give it to be understood that he has definitely chosen England for his home, we do not see how the Academy can help electing him an Associate in their general assembly next week'. (In fact Sargent was not elected to the Academy until January 1894. Thereafter he gave it his unstinting support). Lady Agnew's pose was repeated by Sargent in many portraits in the following

38 *Eleonora Duse*

years together with variations. The culmination of his female sitters in repose is
probably *The Wyndham Sisters* (1899;
Metropolitan Museum of Art, New York).
Other artists were quick to seize on Sargent's
ingenuity and to follow his lead.

38 *Eleonora Duse* (also called *Lady with White Waistcoat*) c.*1893*

Oil on canvas, 58.5 × 48.2 (23 × 19)

Provenance: Artist's sale, Christie's, 24 and
27 July 1925 (lot 137), bought Scott &
Fowles; Mrs Stevenson Scott; Harold
Hecht

Exhibitions: Carfax Gallery, London, 1903;
Venice Biennale, 1934 (24); Washington
1964 (59)

Literature: repr. Meynell 1903, 1927;
Downes 1925, p.259; Charteris 1927, pp.158,
278; M. Birnbaum, *John Singer Sargent*
(1941), pp.23–4, plate 2; Mckibbin 1956,
p.93 (dated 1893); Mount 1969, p.437
(9510) (dated 1895); Ormond 1970, p.248,
plate 68

Lent by Mr and Mrs Paul Amir

Eleonora Duse (1859–1924), the celebrated
Italian tragic actress, whose power of
arousing emotion and whose strange romantic personality created a legend. Sargent
admired her intensely, exclaiming after a
performance of *Feodora* in 1893, during her
first season in London, 'It's terrific!' The
portrait, which must have been executed
around that time, is one of a group of
theatrical personalities whom Sargent
painted at the turn of the nineties, including
Ellen Terry as Lady Macbeth (Tate Gallery,
London), *Henry Irving* (destroyed), *Edwin
Booth* (Players Club, New York), and
Joseph Jefferson (no.36). Sargent only had
one brief sitting from Duse (as she was
always known), but he conjures up her
power and mystique with marvellous effect.
According to Alice Meynell, 'the eyes,
under their sombre lids, have in this brief
sketch, the most direct look in the world.
The great tragedian gives in her portrait, as
in her art, the impression of an incomparable
sincerity and faces us from the yonder side
of the common human custom of inter-
cepted, veiled, retreating or hesitating looks'.
Sargent himself described the single sitting
to Evan Charteris: 'She arrived at midday
and at five minutes to one rose from her

39 *Coventry Patmore*

chair saying, "Je vous souhaite de vivre
mille ans et d'avoir la gloire et beaucoup
d'enfants, mais au revoir", and he never
saw her again.' A related drawing, inscribed
to Henschel, belongs to Francis Neilson.

39 *Coventry Patmore 1894*

Colour plate VI, facing page 17

Oil on canvas, 91.5 × 61 (36 × 24)

Signed and dated (top left and right):
John S. Sargent 1894

Provenance: Presented to the National
Portrait Gallery by the widow of the sitter,
1897

Exhibitions: R.A., 1895 (172); London 1926
(58); *Le Livre Anglais*, Bibliothèque
Nationale, Paris, 1951–2 (ex-catalogue);
Bicentenary Exhibition, R.A., London, 1968–9
(410); *Faces as Art*, NPG, London, 1977

Literature: *Academy*, XLVII (11 May 1895),
p.407; *Athenaeum*, no.3530 (22 June 1895),
p.811; *Magazine of Art* (1895), p.281; *The
Times* (4 May 1895), p.12; B. Champneys,
Memoirs and Correspondence of Coventry Patmore
(1900), I, pp.342, 389–90, and II, p.260,
frontis.; *Scribner's Magazine*, XXXIV (1903),
p.526; repr. Meynell 1903, 1927; Downes
1925, pp.173–4; Charteris 1927, pp.140,

153–4, 174, 265; F. J. Patmore, 'Coventry
Patmore: A Son's Recollections', *English
Review* (February 1932), p.138; D. Patmore,
Coventry Patmore (1949), pp.5–6, 208–10,
226; Mckibbin 1956, p.115; Mount 1969,
pp.209, 447 (945); Ormond 1970, pp.52, 56,
249–50, fig.22 (detail)

Lent by the National Portrait Gallery,
London

Coventry Patmore (1823–96), the Victorian
poet and writer, best remembered now for
his poems in praise of married love, *The
Angel in the House*. He was a figure of impressive character, aloof, sensitive and
passionate. His friend and fellow author,
Edmund Gosse (see no.26), described his
appearance (D. Patmore, op.cit. p.6):
'Three things were particularly noticeable
in the head of Coventry Patmore – the vast
convex brows, arched with vision; the
bright, shrewd, blueish-grey eyes, the outer
fold of one eyelid permanently and humour-
ously drooping and the wilful, sensuous
mouth'.

It was Gosse who urged Patmore to sit
for his portrait to Sargent, who had ex-
pressed an interest in painting the great
poet. Among the Gosse papers at the
Brotherton Library, Leeds, is one from
Sargent of 10 May 1894 thanking Gosse for
Patmore's address. In a letter of 9 May 1894
Patmore told Gosse that he considered
Sargent 'to be the greatest, not only of
living English portrait painters, but of all
English portrait painters, and to be *thus*
invited to sit to him for my picture is among
the most signal honours I have ever received'
(Champneys, op.cit. II, p.260). The portrait
was painted in London during the summer
of 1894, and a series of passages from
contemporary letters describe its progress
(quoted by D. Patmore, op.cit. p.208).
Patmore wrote to his wife: 'The portrait is
fearfully like. It is quite ferocious at present',
and later, 'He is doing his work *con amore*,
and will not leave it off until he has done his
best. He has wonderfully softened the
expression but he says it is still "too ag-
gressive".' Patmore was able to reassure his
wife that he would not be shown smoking a
cigarette, 'The ferocity likewise has dis-
appeared'. He announced the completion of
the portrait in a letter of 9 September to
Gosse (Champneys, op.cit. II, p.260).

The picture is one of Sargent's most
striking male portraits. The lean body,
emphasized by the narrow kit-kat format, is

full of nervous energy, a clenched fist resting decisively on his hip. The scrawny neck, rising out of an old fashioned wing collar, is indicative of Patmore's physical frailty, but the head brilliantly conveys his indomitable and visionary spirit. None of Patmore's friends could deny the truth and power of Sargent's characterization, but it was felt by some to be one-sided.

F. J. Patmore, the poet's son, said that Sargent engaged his father in political argument in order to produce an indignant pose, and Gosse insisted that Patmore was 'not always thus ragged and vulturine, not always such a miraculous portent of gnarled mandible and shaken plumage'. (Charteris 1927, p.153.) To Champneys it seemed 'to incline towards caricature, and to present a somewhat truculent character, alert and active, rather than reflective, thus missing the aspect of "seer" which, in later years, had alone seemed characteristic of him'. When Champneys suggested to Patmore that if the portrait had been extended downwards he would have been revealed with a whip, as some sort of Southern planter about to thrash his slaves, the poet replied, 'Is that not what I have been doing all my life?'

The portrait made a considerable impact at the Royal Academy. The *Athenaeum* called it 'a brilliant sketch, a little exaggerated as a rendering of character, remarkably firm in touch, and displaying excellent colour in a low key, true to the dress and flesh tints of the distinguished poet and essayist'. The *Magazine of Art* was even more laudatory: 'Undoubtedly the most electrifying portrait in the Academy – we nearly wrote the most masterly painting – is Mr Sargent's kit-kat of Mr Coventry Patmore . . . The drawing of the face in Mr Sargent's picture, the brilliant rendering of the mouth – indeed, of the whole mask – are hardly to be matched in any other work of the year. The forehead may not have been treated with the respect traditionally due to planes; yet not only the head, but the figure and garments, have been rendered with an almost unsurpassable skill, and contain passages which would not do discredit to a great master'.

As well as the kit-kat Sargent also painted a head-and-shoulders portrait of Patmore, which he exhibited at the same Academy (formerly Matsukata collection, Japan). Mckibbin mistakenly lists this portrait and one formerly belonging to the National

40 *Coventry Patmore*

Museum of Occidental Art, Tokyo, as two separate works. A profile sketch of Patmore, for one of the prophets in the Boston Library murals, is also exhibited here (no.40).

40 *Coventry Patmore 1894*

Oil on canvas, 47 × 33 (18½ × 13)

Inscribed by the artist on an old label on the back: [sk]etch of Mr Coventry Patmore for / prophet- / to be returned to London

Provenance: The artist's sale, Christie's, 24 and 27 July 1925 (lot 150), bought in; Violet Ormond; thence by family descent

Exhibitions: Possibly Copley Hall, Boston, 1899 (62); London 1926 (442); Tate Gallery 1926, cat. p.7; Birmingham 1964 (24)

Literature: B. Champneys, *Memoirs and Correspondence of Coventry Patmore* (1900), II, repr. facing p.58; Charteris 1927, pp.154, 265; D. Patmore, *Coventry Patmore* (1949), p.209, repr. facing p.208; Mckibbin 1956, p.115 (where lot 150 in the artist's sale is mistakenly identified as a separate work); Mount 1969, pp.209, 210, 447 (943); Ormond 1970, pp.90, 249–50, plate 80

Lent by the Ormond Family

While painting the portrait of Coventry Patmore (no.39), Sargent was so impressed by his sitter's eagle-like profile that he decided to use him as the model for one of the prophets in his scheme of mural decoration in the Boston Public Library. Sargent had first begun work on this Boston cycle, which illustrates the development of religious thought, in 1890. By 1894 he was at work on his frieze of prophets, a series of nineteen monumental figures running below the lunette on the north wall of the upper corridor (installed 1895). Patmore figures as the prophet Ezekiel, a white-robed figure to the left of Daniel, Elijah and Moses.

The profile sketch exhibited here was the study for the head of Ezekiel, which it closely resembles. It is a marvellous essay in bravura painting, the sweeping brushstrokes conjuring up form and character in a seemingly effortless way. But the profile pose, with its classical associations, is a traditional image for the poet, and there is no doubt that in Sargent's sketch Patmore takes on a heroic stature. With his head thrust forward out of his high wing collar he appears transfigured, at a moment of inspiration.

Downes 1925 (p.174) and Charteris 1927 both suggest that the portrait shown at Copley Hall was the one formerly in the Matsukata collection, Japan, but it could equally well have been this sketch; the label on the back of the sketch presumably refers to the Boston or another exhibition.

41 *Mrs Carl Meyer and her Children 1896*

Colour plate VII, facing page 32

Oil on canvas, 209.9 × 135.9 (79½ × 53½)

Signed and dated (bottom left and right): *John S. Sargent 1896*

Provenance: By family descent

Exhibitions: R.A., 1897 (291); Copley Hall, Boston, 1899 (15); Exposition Universelle, Paris, 1900; Tate Gallery 1926, cat. p.7; London 1926 (331), repr. 'Souvenir', p.49; Birmingham 1964 (25), repr.; *English Portraits*, National Museum of Western Art, Tokyo, 1975 (63)

Literature: *Academy*, LI (8 May 1897), p.502; *Art Journal* (1897), p.180; *Black and White*, XIII (8 May 1897), p.579; *Graphic*, LV (1 May 1897), p.530; *Illustrated London News*, CX (8 May 1897), p.645; *Magazine of Art*

(1897), pp.58, 169, and (1899), p.119; *Spectator* (22 May 1897), p.732; *Saturday Review*, LXXXIII (1897), p.572; *The Times* (1 May 1897), p.14; *Studio*, XIX (1900), p.11, repr.; *Scribner's Magazine*, XXXIV (1903), p.529, and LXXV (1924), p.348; repr. Meynell 1903, 1927; E. Fuchs, *With Pencil, Brush and Chisel* (1925), p.32; Downes 1925, pp.41, 49, 178; Charteris 1927, pp.174, 266; *Henry Adams and his Friends*, ed. H. D. Cater (1947), p.404; Mckibbin 1956, p.109; Henry James, *The Painter's Eye*, ed. J. L. Sweeney (1956), pp.254, 256, 257; Mount 1969. pp.222, 446 (968); Ormond 1970, pp.51, 249, plate 77; Adeline R. Tintner, 'Sargent in the fiction of Henry James', *Apollo*, CII (August 1975), pp.129, 131, repr.; John Sunderland, *Painting in Britain 1525 to 1575* (1976), p.241, plate 179

Lent by Sir Anthony Meyer, Bt

Mrs Carl Meyer, née Adèle Levis, was the wife of the naturalized English banker, Carl Meyer (created a baronet in 1910). Her children were Frank, later 2nd Baronet, and Elsie (later Mrs St John Lambert, secondly, Mrs Harry Hulbert). Lady Meyer and her husband were renowned hosts and patrons of the arts.

This portrait is one of Sargent's most successful depictions of seated women. The pose of the principal subject derives from *Mrs Hugh Hammersley* (1893; private collection). The perspective is dramatically foreshortened so that the figure is brought forward and her immense ballooning peach-coloured dress fills most of the foreground. The eye is led into the composition by way of her arm and the back of the sofa to the children behind. Mrs Meyer's natural vivacity is emphasized by the enormous panache with which the symbols of Edwardian wealth are expressed: the *boiseries* and Louis XV sofa, the satins and velvets of the clothes, the abandoned book, and, above all, the strings of pearls which amply reach the foot-stool. The contrasting characters of the mother and children are brilliantly realized by compressing the shy children into the corner, half-hidden behind the gilded sofa, while the expansive character of their mother is emphasized by her voluminous dress and fully extended fan. The whole tone of the picture is entirely unapologetic, and Sargent has created a dazzling image of *fin de siècle* opulence which was to be repeated in the series of portraits of the Wertheimer family (no.46).

41 *Mrs Carl Meyer and her Children*

The impact made by this picture when it was exhibited at the Royal Academy was sensational. The hostile Henry Adams wrote: 'But just now we all go to the Royal Academy to see Sargent's portrait of Mrs Mayer [*sic*] and her two children. Mrs Mayer is a sprightly Jewess, who did us the favor to stand under her portrait on the private opening day to show that she was as good as her picture. The art of portrait-painting of Jewesses and their children may be varied but cannot be further perfected. Nothing better ever was done or can be done'. Sargent's old friend Henry James reviewed the Academy for *Harper's Weekly*, and wrote: 'Mr Sargent has made a picture of knock-down insolence of talent and truth of characterization, a wonderful rendering of life, of manners, of aspects, of types, of textures, of everything . . . Beside him, at any rate, his competitors appear to stammer . . .'

Sargent's position as the pre-eminent portrait painter of his day was possibly established finally by this picture. The writer in *The Times* recognized this: ' . . . he [Sargent] seems to have reached a point in his art where certainty takes the place of experiment and assured possession that of revolt. In the case of the group, we have, of course, to admit certain conditions; it represents a highly artificial moment of civilization; it is of the world, worldly; we are in the midst of an atmosphere of silks and satins and old French furniture, and we have to do with what Lothair called "ropes of pearls". Lothair's creator [Disraeli] would indeed have rejoiced in the picture, and would have devoted to it half-a-dozen scintillating sentences in his next novel. But, after all, the great painters of every age have painted the wealthy society of their time . . .'

42 *Mrs George Swinton 1896–7*

Colour plate VIII, facing page 33

Oil on canvas, 228.6 × 124.5 (90 × 49)

Signed (bottom left): *John S. Sargent*

Provenance: Bought from Captain Swinton via Knoedler by the Art Institute of Chicago, 1922

Exhibitions: New Gallery, London, 1897 (245); Royal Scottish Academy, 1917; Art Institute of Chicago, 1922 (202); Cincinnati Art Museum, 1922 (38); Boston 1925 (97); New York, 1926 (29)

Literature: *Academy*, LI (1 May 1897), p.479; *Athenaeum*, no.3630 (22 May 1897), p.687; *Illustrated London News*, CX (1 May 1897), p.608; *Saturday Review*, LXXXIII (15 May 1897), p.538; *Spectator*, LXXVIII (1 May 1897) p.625; *The Times* (24 April 1897), p.10; *AIC Annual Report* (1922), pp.40, 53; *AIC Bulletin* XVI (1922), pp.89, 92; *International Studio*, LXXVI (1922), p.211, repr.; Downes 1925, pp.179–80, repr. facing p.160; Charteris 1927, p.266; *Art Digest*, XXIII (15 February 1949), repr. p.8; Mckibbin 1956, p.125; *AIC Catalogue* (1961), p.411; Mount 1969, pp.267, 453 (969), repr.; John Maxon, *The Art Institute of Chicago* (1970), pp.269, 285, repr.; Ormond 1970, p.52; D. A. Hanks, 'American Paintings at the AIC', *The Magazine Antiques*, I (1973), pp.895–905, repr.; forthcoming AIC catalogue with more detailed bibliography

Lent by the Art Institute of Chicago (Wirt D. Walker Fund)

Mrs George Swinton, née Elsie Ebsworth, married Captain George Swinton in 1895. Her husband was to become an official at the Royal College of Heralds, an influential figure in the London County Council and Chairman of the Delhi Town Planning

Committee (Sargent's drawing of him, 1912, is at County Hall, London). Mrs Swinton possessed a very fine singing voice (see no.62), and they were friends of other younger artists including Orpen, Sickert and Spencer Gore.

The circumstances of this commission are particularly well recorded, despite Sargent's habit of not dating his letters. He was approached by Captain Swinton, on behalf of Mrs Ebsworth, early in 1895 to paint his fiancée, and replied on 26 March that he was delighted that 'it is to be a full length which gives me more of a chance to do an interesting picture. I am leaving for America on the 6th April and expect to be back in June – so that July would be the earliest time I can hope to begin.' In fact Sargent was delayed in America owing to his mother's illness, and returned to England via Spain somewhat later and was immediately taken up with the Boston mural decorations. Sittings were postponed until after the birth of Mrs Swinton's son in March 1896 and began the following month. Sargent wrote (letter postmarked 11 April 1896): 'I shall expect you on Tuesday morning between 11 and 1. The more dresses to choose from the better. I was sorry you could not come on picture Sunday, you would have seen things of different shapes and sizes. Mrs Ebsworth seemed in doubt as to whether it ought to be a full-length or not.'

The portrait advanced very slowly. According to a letter written years later by Mrs Swinton (cited by Downes 1925, p.180), 'it took a great many sittings, as we wasted a lot of time playing the piano and singing, instead of getting on with the picture.' It was still incomplete by 9 January 1897, when Sargent left for Sicily for a few weeks. He arranged a sitting for 2 March by a note from Florence dated 26 February 1897, and the picture was evidently complete for the New Gallery exhibition in May. A letter from Sargent to Mrs Ebsworth of 3 May 1897, thanking her for payment, belongs to Mrs A. H. Sutherland.

This portrait is one of the most successful full-lengths of the 1890s, and is one of a small group representing certain common features, including *Ada Rehan* (1894; Metropolitan Museum of Art, New York) and *Mrs Roller* (1895; private collection). Like *Lady Agnew* (no.37), the figure is considered in terms of decorative effect, the modelling of the head is extremely subtle

42 *Mrs George Swinton*

and the dress is in the boldest manner. The taut features of Sargent's early style, seen in the portraits of *Madame X* (no.13) and *Mrs Robert Harrison* (no.27), have been superseded by the freedom of impressionism, and it is instructive to compare the treatment of shimmering light falling over the white silk dress with the same feature in *Mrs Henry White* (no.12). Sargent's use of furniture in this portrait is mainly to enhance the colour scheme and not merely a compositional device.

The picture was received with only slightly less acclaim by the critics at the New Gallery than *Mrs Carl Meyer and her Children* (no.41) at the Royal Academy the same year. The reviewer in the *Spectator* wrote: 'Even if there is nothing new in the arrangement of the figure and the accessories, still the fact that no one else can paint these things in a manner even approaching to Mr Sargent makes one glad to see them again, when painted with such convincing mastery . . . One wonders if anyone else could have painted the left arm – or rather

left it out – with such complete feeling of the solid structure beneath the loose scarf . . . nevertheless by the subtlety of the drawing of the folds of satin the presence of the limb is distinctly felt. It is by these resources of the art of suggestion that the painter has made his canvas seem alive . . . There is a great gap between this splendid piece of *bravura* and the attempt at a like style by Mr Shannon.'

The picture was awarded the Potter Palmer Gold Medal and a prize of one thousand dollars when exhibited in Chicago, and was bought in consequence by the Art Institute. A copy of the director's letter of 8 November 1922 to Sargent announcing the award and purchase is in the Institute's archives.

43 *The Hon Victoria Stanley 1899*

Colour plate IX, facing page 48

Oil on canvas, 196.8 × 105.4 (77½ × 41½)

Signed and dated (top right): *John S. Sargent 1899*

Exhibitions: New Gallery, London, 1900 (248); London 1926 (421); Birmingham 1964 (30)

Provenance: The Earl of Derby; thence by family descent

Literature: *Athenaeum*, no.3783 (28 April 1900), p.534; *Spectator*, LXXXV (28 April 1900), p.599; *Illustrated London News*, CXVI (5 May 1900), p.597; *Magazine of Art* (1900), p.392; *Art Journal* (1900), p.186; *The Times* (23 April 1900), p.8; *Saturday Review*, LXXXIX (1900), p.555; *Nineteenth Century*, CCXCII (June 1901), p.1023; repr. Meynell 1903, 1927; Downes 1925, pp.191–2; Charteris 1927, p.268; Mckibbin 1956, p.124; Mount 1969, p.452 (996)

Lent anonymously

The Hon (later Lady) Victoria Stanley was the daughter of the 17th Earl of Derby. She married first Lord Primrose, son of the Prime Minister the Earl of Rosebery, who died of wounds in 1917, and secondly Sir Malcolm Bullock, Bt. The portrait was painted when the sitter was seven years old.

Sargent told a previous owner of this picture that he considered it the finest portrait of a child he had ever done. Indeed, Sargent's ability to capture a child's personality and expression ranges from the highly-charged *Pailleron Children* (1881; Armand J. Hammer collection), and the Infanta-like treatment of *Beatrice Goelet* (1890; private collection), to the unmistakably American image of *Beatrice Townsend* (1882; Mellon collection). In this portrait the natural ebullience of the little girl is brilliantly suggested in the strikingly novel pose; the oversized hat and jacket add to the effect of spontaneity. The colour arrangements of the picture are symphonic reds and whites, repeated in the Aubusson carpet. The strong directed lighting makes the composition reminiscent of *Doctor Pozzi* (1881; Armand J. Hammer collection).

The late Sir Osbert Sitwell was also seven years old when he posed for Sargent to be included in the *Sitwell Family* (1900; private collection). In his biography, *Left Hand, Right Hand!* (1945), he recalled Sargent's kindness: 'Certainly he was very patient, would go to almost any trouble, consistent with being allowed to paint, to amuse us. When the first fascination of watching him at work, a conjuror drawing effects out of the void, had worn off, we became restless – especially Sacheverell who was only two years old . . . but Sargent could always contrive to hold his attention for a few extra minutes, either by indulging in a peculiar and elaborate whistling he had cultivated, like that of a French *siffleur* upon the music-hall stage, or by innocently intoning a limerick, which ran:

> There was a Young Lady of Spain
> Who often was sick in a train,
> Not once and again,
> But again and again,
> And again and again and again.'

Sargent's inventiveness is probably at its strongest around 1900, for in that year he exhibited such diverse portraits as *The Wyndham Sisters, Lord Russell of Killowen,* and *General Ian Hamilton*. This portrait was shown at the New Gallery and was almost universally acclaimed. The critic of *The Times* was probably the most perspicacious: 'The simplicity of this portrait is half its charm. The other half lies in the colour of the whole composition, in the alertness of the little figure, and in the bonny freshness of the child's face. Seldom has Mr Sargent given us so much positive colour – red without a hint of decadence, set over against a cream white, that is dazzling in its brilliancy. The eyes, too, sparkle with life and are brimming with laughter. It is only after you have seen and enjoyed these essentials of the picture that you begin to look closer and ask

43 *The Hon Victoria Stanley*

how it is done – how the brush of the painter has moved to its achievement, and then you perceive the extraordinary sureness and rapidity of the touch. A single stroke and a large flat surface is realized; another, and this time with the handle of the brush, and the shadowy fold is there, exactly right in its direction and its gradations of lighter and deeper shade. Amazing, but how dangerous an example! . . . the imitators of Sargent need be nothing but clever manipulators, with a resolution to *épater le bourgeois*. Every Salon shows how they do it; and the English exhibitions are beginning to show it too.' The correspondent in the *Saturday Review* showed rather less taste: 'A rather savage Sargent. Imagine a portrait of Little Red Riding Hood by the Wolf.'

44 *The Earl of Dalhousie 1900*

Oil on canvas, 152.4 × 101.6 (60 × 40)

Signed (top left): *John S. Sargent*

Provenance: The sitter; thence by family descent

Exhibition: R.A., 1900 (44)

Literature: *Athenaeum*, no.3789 (9 June 1900), p.726; *Magazine of Art* (1900), p.385, repr. p.389; *Royal Academy Pictures* (1900), repr. p.64; *Art Journal* (1900), pp.166–8; *Spectator*, LXXXV (26 May 1900); *The Times* (5 May 1900), p.14; *Graphic*, LXI (12 May 1900), p.698; *Saturday Review*, LXXXIX (1900), p.583; *Vanity Fair* (10 May 1900), p.327; Downes 1925, p.190; Charteris 1927, p.268; Mckibbin 1956, p.91; Mount 1969, p.436 (006); *Country Life*, CL (19 August 1971), repr. p.439

Lent by the Rt Hon the Earl of Dalhousie, KT

Exhibited Leeds and London only

Arthur George Maule Ramsay succeeded his father as 14th Earl of Dalhousie in 1887. He served in the South African War, 1901–2, with distinction and was wounded in the First World War.

Sargent has depicted the young earl in an architectural setting with a darkened background, and the subject is dressed in cream-coloured tropical clothes and a red tie, heightening the complex tonal relationships. This is one of Sargent's earliest essays in placing his subject against columns and pilasters, which was to become a feature of his male portraits in years to come, notably *Lord Ribblesdale* (1902; Tate Gallery, London) and *A. J. Balfour* (no.51). The source for this type of formal portrait descends from Van Dyck and Reynolds, and it here marks Sargent's coming to terms with an identifiable 'British' type of portraiture. The subject should be contrasted with that of the later *Sir Frank Swettenham* (no.49), who regales the spectator with the full repertoire of imperial iconography. Here the impact is one of youthful and aristocratic self-confidence, rare among Sargent's male portraits. The naturalness of the pose acts as a foil to the imposing architectural backdrop; the subject has one arm resting in front of a column and the other on his hip, and the head is carefully drawn, revealing a knowledgeable characterization. The handling of the brushwork is bold and vigorous, reminiscent of the broad passages in *The Hon Victoria Stanley* (no.43) and the *Acheson Sisters* (no.47).

Although the critics at the Royal Academy of 1900 reserved most of their praises for the sensational *Wyndham Sisters* (Metropolitan Museum of Art, New York), described by the Prince of Wales as 'the Three Graces', many recommended this portrait. The *Spectator* commented: 'Those who appreciate Mr Sargent's art should not miss his portrait of *The Earl of Dalhousie*. The success of the realism is complete; only a real master could have succeeded in making the young face look perfectly right with the sun burn ending in a diagonal line across the forehead. This is not done to give an air of audacity to the painting but is simply the way in which a master seizes on things that help him in his characterization'.

45 *The Hon Mrs Charles Russell* *1900*

Oil on canvas, 105.4 × 74.9 (41½ × 29½)

Signed and dated (bottom left): *John S. Sargent 1900*

Provenance: Sir Charles Russell, Bt; thence by family descent

Exhibitions: R.A., 1901 (219); London 1926 (55)

Literature: *The Times* (4 May 1901), p.13; *Magazine of Art* (1901), p.388; *Art Journal* (1901), p.180; *Graphic*, LXIII (18 May 1901), p.674; *Illustrated London News*, CXVIII (11 May 1901), suppl. VIII; *Saturday Review*, XCI (1901), p.632; *Spectator* (25 May 1901), p.768; *Athenaeum*, no.3837 (11 May 1901), p.601; Downes 1925, p.194; *Scribner's Magazine*, LXXV (1924), pp.242, 348, repr.; repr. Meynell 1903, 1927; Charteris 1927, pp.175, 268; Mckibbin 1956, p.121; Mount 1969, p.450 (005)

Lent by Sir Charles Russell, Bt

Mrs Charles Russell, née Adah Williams, was the granddaughter of Sir Joshua Walmsley, one of the founders of the *Daily News*. She married Charles Russell (later created a baronet), a solicitor with responsibility for the British Agent in the Behring Sea Arbitration (1893) and for the Government of Canada, and also for the Stewards of the Jockey Club. Sargent's portrait of Mrs Russell is in distinct contrast to his more flamboyant pictures of this period, and it represents a sensitivity to character quite different from his preferred

44 *The Earl of Dalhousie*

types. The subject is dressed in a gown with subtle transitions from pink to pearl-grey, and the head is seen in a half-tone while her hair merges into the background darkness. The effect of elongation is stressed by the pose of the arms and the lampstand behind her (still in the possession of the Ormond family). It is an intensely aristocratic image strengthened by her expression of melancholy, and may derive from Romney or Greuze. Many critics at the Royal Academy of 1901 contrasted this portrait with the vivacious pair, *Ena and Betty Wertheimer* (no.46). The correspondent in the *Graphic* wrote: 'The face is of extraordinary character, infinite pathos, and a masterpiece of painting . . . it haunts us, with its sad eyes and intellectual distress.'

Sargent also painted *Baron Russell of Killowen*, Mrs Russell's father-in-law and the first Roman Catholic Lord Chief Justice of England since the Reformation (Lincoln's Inn and Russell family; a replica of the latter is in the National Portrait Gallery, London). There are two drawings of Mrs Russell – in the Museum of Fine Arts, Boston, and the Fogg Art Museum, Cambridge, Mass.

46 *Ena and Betty, Daughters of Asher and Mrs Wertheimer 1901*

Oil on canvas, 185.5 × 131 (73 × 51½)

Signed and dated (bottom right): *John S. Sargent 1901*

Provenance: Presented to the National Gallery by the widow and family of Asher Wertheimer, in accordance with his wishes, 1922; transferred to the Tate Gallery, 1926

Exhibitions: R.A., 1901 (178); New Salon, Paris, 1902

Literature: *Athenaeum*, no.3837 (11 May 1901), p.601; *Guardian*, no.2892 (8 May 1901), p.621; *Magazine of Art* (1901), p.388; *Nineteenth Century*, CCXCII (1901), pp.1023–4; *R. A. Pictures* (1901), repr. p.132; *Saturday Review*, XCI (18 May 1901), pp.632–3; *Spectator*, LXXXVI (25 May 1901), pp.767–8; *The Times* (4 May 1901), p.13; *Gazette des Beaux Arts*, XXVIII (1902), repr. facing p.64; *Scribner's Magazine*, XXXIV (1903), p.530; R. Ross, 'The Wertheimer Sargents', *Art Journal* (1911), p.8, repr. p.5; Downes 1925, pp.46, 193, repr. facing p.200; Charteris 1927, pp.164–5, 269, repr. facing p.166; *The Times* (27 March 1936), p.17; Mckibbin 1956, p.130; *Tate Gallery Catalogue: The Modern*

45 *The Hon Mrs Charles Russell*

British Paintings, Drawings and Sculpture, II (1964), pp.595–6; Mount 1969, pp.225, 456 (017); Ormond 1970, pp.65, 254, plate 97

Lent by the Tate Gallery

The daughters of Sargent's great patron, Asher Wertheimer: on the left Betty (later Mrs Eustace Salaman, secondly Mrs Arthur Ricketts), and on the right Ena (later Mrs Robert Mathias). Sargent had painted Asher himself, the prominent Bond Street art dealer, in 1898, and during the course of the next few years he painted a succession of Wertheimer portraits which were given to the nation. To Roger Fry it was something quite new 'in the history of civilization that such a man should venture to have himself and the members of his numerous family portrayed on the scale and with the circumstances of a royal or ducal family', and he recognized in Sargent unique gifts for combining 'decorative splendour and *éclat*' with a 'dispassionate and terribly observant eye.'

While it is true that Sargent presents his sitters without flattery, and with all the attributes of social status, it must be remembered that he was a close friend of the Wertheimer family, and that he admired their beauty, talent and high spirits. The extrovert Ena was a particular favourite, volatile, unconventional, and passionately keen on art and music. Sargent was later to paint her dressed up in the Garter hat and robes of Lord Londonderry, calling the spirited result *A Vele Gonfie* (in full sail) (private collection).

It is a tribute to Sargent's admiration for the sisters that *Ena and Betty* is such an uninhibited *tour de force*. One has the feeling that the two girls have just stepped into the room, the taller Ena still holding her sister slightly awkwardly round the waist, and steadying herself against an enormous Chinese vase. The opulent setting of the Wertheimer drawing-room at Connaught Place is suggested by a few objects seen in the dim but atmospheric space behind: a Louis Seize commode with a celadon bowl and cover mounted in ormulu (both still in the possession of Wertheimer descendants), the big but obscure picture over it with what appears to be a heavily draped figure coming forward, the Dutch(?) landscape on the left and the frame of another picture above. And the girls, in contrasting dresses of dark red velvet and white satin, are themselves *objets de luxe*. But what is re-

46 *Ena and Betty, Daughters of Asher and Mrs Wertheimer*

Colour plate **XI**
The Duchess of Portland 1902 (no.48)

Colour plate XII
Sir Frank Swettenham 1904 (no.49)

markable about the picture is not its accessories or even its design but the intense feeling of life which it communicates. The relationship between the two girls is not forced, and the character of each is vividly given: the feminine allure of the younger, the arm holding the fan sinuously out-turned like that of *Madame X* (no.13), the overwhelming vitality of her sister.

People at the time were amazed by the portrait's actuality, its brilliant execution and disregard of portrait conventions. Reviewers at the Academy raved about it, and even the normally hostile Roger Fry called it 'in its way a masterpiece'. The most extended critique came from D. S. MacColl in the *Saturday Review*:

I should say that rarely in the history of painting have its engines discharged a portrait so emphatically so undistractedly contrived. The woman [Ena] is there, with a vitality hardly matched since Rubens, the race, the social type, the person. And design, which only comes to Mr Sargent when he is excited by the batteries or entranced by the strangeness of light, has come in not to crib contradict or excuse the two figures, but to push conviction further, a design discovered in the material, the sway of one figure to the other, and the run of light along the turned out arm and downstroke of the fan. Turn to the other portrait [*Mrs Charles Russell*, no.45], and observe how these two pictures are designed, and designed for the imagination, in three dimensions. Not merely are they the only pictures on the walls that give the third dimension, so that soft shady space seems to open back from their frames among canvases merely mottled with flat dark and light, but this third dimension is used dramatically to express character.

47 *The Acheson Sisters 1902*

Colour plate x, facing page 49

Oil on canvas, 269.2 × 198 (106 × 78)

Signed and dated (bottom right): *John S. Sargent 1902*

Provenance: The Duchess of Devonshire; thence by family descent

Exhibitions: R.A., 1902 (89); Franco-British Exhibition, London, 1902; International Fine Arts Exhibition, Rome, 1911 (313); Venice, 1907 (28); Berlin,

47 *The Acheson Sisters*

1908; London 1926 (573), repr. 'Souvenir', p.3; York Art Gallery, 1926 (29)

Literature: *Athenaeum*, no. 3889 (10 May 1902), p.600; *Academy*, LXII (10 May 1902), p.488; *Spectator*, LXXXVIII (3 May 1902), p.687; *Magazine of Art* (1902), p.356; *Art Journal* (1902), p.209; *The Times* (3 May 1902), p.16; *Black and White*, XXIII (17 May 1902), p.706; *Graphic*, LXV (3 May 1902), p.595; *Saturday Review*, XCIII (1902), p.595; *Studio*, XXVI (1902), p.26; *Scribner's Magazine*, LXXV (1924), p.352; Downes 1925, pp.202–3, repr. facing p.232; repr. Meynell 1927; Charteris 1927, pp.68, 177, 270; Mckibbin 1956, p.81; Mount 1969, p.430 (0218); Ormond 1970, p.65; Richard Shone, *The Century of Change: British painting since 1900* (1977), repr.

Lent by the Trustees of the Chatsworth Settlement

The Ladies Alexandra, Mary and Theodosia Acheson were the daughters of the 4th Earl of Gosford and granddaughters of Duchess Louisa of Devonshire by her first marriage with the 7th Duke of Manchester. After their marriages they became Lady Alexandra Stanley, Lady Mary Ward and Lady Theodosia Cadogan respectively. It is not known how this picture came to be commissioned, but it is extremely likely that Duchess Louisa commissioned it

specifically for Chatsworth.

This group is probably the most self-consciously 'learned' in Sargent's oeuvre and can be considered as a homage to Reynolds. In 1923 Sargent gave an address to the Royal Academy on the bicentenary of Sir Joshua's birthday. He spoke of his own admiration for Reynolds: 'It must be left to individual taste to choose which most to admire, the simpler portraits like, among many others, the portentous head of Dr Johnson, so grand in character and suggestion, or those more fanciful compositions in which Sir Joshua invested a portrait with all the charm of a decorative picture. His resources in this line were unbounded, and the setting, however romantic, in which he sometimes placed his people never detracted from their interest as men and women.'

It is difficult to find an immediate source for this composition but the figure to the left is an obvious derivation from Reynolds's *Marchioness of Tavistock*. It should be noted that several late-nineteenth-century artists plagiarized the eighteenth-century masters, notably Millais in *Hearts are Trumps*, which is based closely on Reynolds's *The Ladies Waldegrave*.

This is one of the earliest examples of Sargent's posing his subjects in an open-air landscape since his impressionist phase. The effect is of course entirely different to the intimate figure scenes of the earlier period. Here the figures are undeniably posed but radiate a mood of *joie de vivre* and innocence. It should be contrasted with the earlier *Wyndham Sisters* (Metropolitan Museum of Art, New York), an interior group of three sisters, where the impression is one of languid splendour. Each figure has a sense of movement and this is emphasized in the figure on the right by her feathered hat and the graceful sweep of her sash. The bold treatment of their white dresses captures the effect of sunlight.

This picture dominated the Royal Academy exhibition of 1902 in the same way that the *Wyndham Sisters* dominated that of 1900. *The Times* added one proviso: 'If there is a fault to be found, it is that the figures, even for these days of tall women, are almost impossibly tall; but waiving this debatable point, we have nothing but praise for this animated, ingenious and really beautiful picture'. The huge vase around which the figures are grouped was a notable feature in Sargent's Tite Street studio.

48 *The Duchess of Portland*

48 *The Duchess of Portland 1902*

Colour plate XI, facing page 64

Oil on canvas, 228.6 × 113 (90 × 44)

Signed and dated (bottom right): *John S. Sargent 1902*

Provenance: 6th Duke of Portland; thence by family descent

Exhibitions: R.A., 1902 (323); Nottingham, 1903 (121); Laing Art Gallery, Newcastle upon Tyne, 1904 (130); London 1926 (288), repr. 'Souvenir', p.79; Usher Art Gallery, Lincoln, 1927; Royal Scottish Academy, 1927; *Fair Women of the Nineteenth Century*, Knoedler, London, 1933 (10)

Literature: *Athenaeum*, no. 3889 (10 May 1902), p.600; *Art Journal* (1902), p.210; *Magazine of Art* (1902), pp.356, 358; *The Times* (3 May 1902), p.16; *Academy*, LXII (10 May 1902), pp.487–8; *Spectator*, LXXXVIII (3 May 1902), p.687; repr. Meynell 1903, 1927; Downes 1925, p.196; Charteris 1927, p.269; Richard W. Goulding and C. K. Adams, *Catalogue of the Pictures belonging to His Grace the Duke of Portland K.G.* (1936), pp.225–6 (559); *Men, Women and Things: Memories of the Duke of Portland K.G., G.C.V.O.* (1937), pp.219–20; Mckibbin 1956, p.117; Mount 1969, pp.230–1, 448 (021); Ormond 1970, p.64

Lent by Lady Anne Bentinck

Exhibited Leeds and London only

The Duchess of Portland, née Winifred Anna Dallas-Yorke, was one of the great beauties of the age. Sargent was a friend of the Portland family and stayed at Welbeck Abbey, the family seat, on a number of occasions.

In 1900 Sargent had painted the 6th Duke in informal sporting clothes with his two collie dogs, and it was probably the success of this that led to the commission to paint the duchess, although the pair could never have been conceived as pendants. Unusually, Sargent travelled to Welbeck to execute the portrait, and this is related by the duke in his *Memories* (op.cit.): 'In 1902 he stayed with us for nearly a month, and during that time he painted the well-known picture of my wife. His first attempt did not at all satisfy him, as he thought he had failed to reproduce the character of his sitter, nor could he make the work *move*, as he termed it, or live. This caused him great annoyance, and very often he filled his brush with paint and then rushed at the picture, muttering strange Spanish oaths. After sitting to him for about a fortnight, my wife came down one morning to find a clean canvas on the easel, and the remains of the picture he had painted slashed right across and lying in a corner of the room. She was so overcome with fatigue and disappointment that she burst into tears; but Sargent reassured her by saying, "I know you so well now that, if only you will let me try again, I am quite sure I can paint something 'alive', which will be a credit to myself and satisfactory to you and your family as well. So pray forgive me, and let me have at least another chance". He then altered her pose . . . He worked in the Gobelins Tapestry Room, and my wife stood against the marble mantlepiece. The picture simply flowed along, and in a very short time was completed. When it was finished the canvas remained in the empty room, and one of our friends – Lady Helen Vincent, now Lady D'Abernon [see no. 61] – who happened to look through the window, tapped on the glass and called my wife's name. Later in the day she met my wife and asked her, "why were you so haughty this morning, and wouldn't answer when I tapped on the window?" Sargent was very pleased when he heard this . . . He was also a beautiful musician, and when not painting or scribbling he delighted in playing the piano . . .'

The duchess's pose is slightly ambiguous and unusual in Sargent's repertoire. The use of fancy-dress, so frequent with Sargent's women sitters, was commented on with favour by the critic of the *Spectator*: 'The extreme simplicity of the colour arrangements gives a clearness of style infinitely delightful in these days of polychromatic clothes in ladies' portraits. Though vigorous and masterly to the last degree, there is not that effrontery of cleverness which Mr Sargent sometimes affects'.

Most of the critics pointed out its place in the Royal Academy exhibition as a pendant to Carolus-Duran's *Mrs Charles S. Henry*. As the *Magazine of Art* put it: 'the superiority of the Anglo-American artist makes one smile at the studio gossip which credits M. Carolus-Duran with warning his pupils against Mr Sargent's degeneracy with the words "Sargent-ca n'existe plus!"'.

49 *Sir Frank Swettenham 1904*

Colour plate XII, facing page 65

Oil on canvas, 170.8 × 110.5 (67¼ × 47½)

Signed and dated (bottom right): *John S. Sargent 1904*

Provenance: Bequeathed to the National Portrait Gallery by the sitter, 1946, with a life interest to his widow, who died in 1971

Exhibition: London 1926 (322), repr. 'Souvenir', p.47

Literature: Charteris 1927, p.271 (where confused with the Singapore portrait); Mckibbin 1956, p.125; Mount 1955, p.438 (049); Ormond 1970, p.253 (note to plate 94); *NPG Report 1967–75* (1976), plate 42

Lent by the National Portrait Gallery, London

Sir Frank Athelstane Swettenham (1850–1946) entered the service of the Straits

49 *Sir Frank Swettenham*

50 *Mrs Huth Jackson*

Settlement in 1871. He did a great deal to further the social and economic progress of Malaya, and had great sympathy with its people and customs. After a successful career he was made Governor of the Malay States in 1901, retiring three years later.

In 1903 the Straits Association in London invited Swettenham to their annual dinner, and the members expressed a wish 'to have my portrait painted by an artist I chose, with the intention of presenting it to the Colony and getting it hung in the Victoria Hall at Singapore, which contained the pictures of a number of my predecessors.' (*Footsteps in Malaya*, 1942, p.141.) It is not known on whose advice Swettenham chose Sargent for this commission, but the two soon became friends, and mutual admirers. 'I sat for him about a dozen times', wrote Swettenham, 'and as he liked talking whilst he painted, I passed many pleasant hours in his studio. He happened to be painting the portraits of a number of my friends, and it was interesting to watch these pictures grow day by day to completion, and hear the discerning comments on the frames of mind in which his sitters presented themselves to a man whose brush recorded characters as well as features.'

The picture exhibited here is a version of the full-length portrait, dated 1904 and exhibited a year later, which was sent to Singapore and is now in the Art Gallery there (repr. Ormond 1970, plate 94, when still unlocated). Sargent had arranged for the original picture to be copied by another artist for Swettenham, possibly J. Cooke, but he was so dissatisfied with the result that he took the copy over, repainting most of the work, and altering the design in the process, most notably the head (for which he received further sittings), the placing of the sitter's right hand and arm, the uniform (altered in accordance with new regulations for governors' uniforms issued by the Colonial Office), and the globe and draperies (information from Lady Swettenham, Brigadier Swettenham, and Mckibbin). The NPG portrait is an original work in its own right, more compressed in design than the big portrait, and more dramatic in its contrast of light and dark.

Swettenham is represented as the epitome of the Edwardian proconsul. Dimly seen above the tropically clad figure is the base and lower section of a huge globe (also used by Sargent in a group portrait of four American doctors of this date), symbol of Empire, and falling over the French *bergère* are the tributes of a subject people, magnificent Malaysian brocades collected by Swettenham himself and now in the museum at Kuala Lumpur. The full-length version also includes an ivory baton (Swettenham's badge of office), unrolled documents, a topi, and a leopard-skin rug. Writing of this last portrait at the 1905 New Gallery exhibition, Frank Rinder commented: 'In portraiture there is nothing comparable, as a brilliant realization of character and accessories, with Mr Sargent's "Sir Frank Swettenham". The lithe military figure, in white linen suit, accustomed to command, has here authority in a composition full of threatening accessories'. (*Art Journal*, 1905, pp.182–3.)

The design, one of Sargent's grandest, certainly owes something to Van Dyck in the heroic conception of the figure, set off by swirling accessories, and in the sonorous colour. But the portrait is held together by the force of Swettenham's personality. That he is more than just a bureaucrat or man of action is suggested in the NPG portrait by the claw-like hands tensely gripping the edge of the chair. What appears to have been a copy of the Singapore portrait, listed by Mckibbin as by J. Cooke, formerly hung in the King's House at Kuala Lumpur; it is said to have been returned to the Crown Agents in London between 1958 and 1961, but is at present untraced. Two later charcoal drawings of Swettenham are recorded, one dated 1919. Swettenham also acquired a number of fine Sargent landscapes in oil and water-colour (sold at Christie's, 22 November 1946).

50 *Mrs Huth Jackson* 1907

Oil on canvas, 147.3 × 99 (58 × 39)

Signed and dated (bottom right): *John S. Sargent 1907*

Provenance: By family descent

Exhibitions: R.A., 1908 (504); London 1926 (52); *Portraits of Personalities Past and Present*, Portraits Inc, New York, 1958 (41), repr. catalogue cover

Literature: Downes 1925, p.231; Charteris 1927, p.274; Mckibbin 1956, p.103; Mount, *Art Quarterly*, 1963, p.409, fig.35; Mount 1969, pp.286, 442 (077); Ormond 1970, p.66; Anne Fremantle, *Three-Cornered Heart*, (1971), pp.227, 240, repr.

Lent by Sheila Sonne

Annabel Huth Jackson (1870–1944), the daughter of Sir Mountstuart Grant Duff, Governor of Madras, and the wife of Frederick Huth Jackson, a director of the Bank of England and a partner of the trading company, Frederick Huth & Company. She was a person of striking personality and good looks, with a great sense of style. She was a gifted hostess and had a wide circle of interesting friends, many of them people of creative or intellectual talent. She described her own unusual upbringing in *A Victorian Childhood* (1932), and is the subject of a sensitive portrait in the autobiography of her daughter, *Three-Cornered Heart* (op.cit.). She and her children remained old friends of the Sargent and Ormond families.

Mrs Jackson is shown in the artist's studio, seated on a Louis Seize sofa, with pilasters behind and a falling curtain. The inventive composition marks a new departure in Sargent's work. C. M. Mount has pointed out the close parallels with Ingres's *Madame Rivière* (Louvre), where the figure is similarly posed in a sinuously draped Cashmere shawl, her elbow resting on a cushion. There is a distinct neo-classical mood to Sargent's picture, with its cool characterization, and its treatment of smooth and luxurious textures. The severe lines of the sofa provide a strong frame to the figure, offset to some extent by the movement of the draperies, from the curtain and cushion behind the sitter's head to the spiralling folds of the shawl and the dress.

The Cashmere shawl was the motif for several other portraits and figure studies of this period (see nos.90 and 91), and it heralds a move towards a more controlled and consciously decorative style. It is interesting to note that this development comes at the very moment when Sargent was abandoning portraiture for good, in favour of mural painting and informal studies and landscapes, where he was freer to experiment. The portrait of Mrs Jackson was overshadowed at the 1908 Academy by Sargent's other contributions, *A. J. Balfour* (no.51), and the *Duke and Duchess of Connaught* (companion portraits; Royal Collection). There are a few glancing allusions to it in contemporary reviews but nothing worth recording.

51 *Arthur James Balfour*

51 *Arthur James Balfour 1908*
(later 1st Earl of Balfour)

Oil on canvas, 256.5 × 147.3 (101 × 58)

Signed and dated (top left and right):
John S. Sargent 1908

Provenance: Commissioned by the Carlton Club

Exhibitions: R.A., 1908 (207); London 1926 (311), repr. 'Souvenir', p.99

Literature: *Art Journal* (1908), pp.162–3; *Athenaeum*, no. 4202 (9 May 1908), p.581; *Spectator*, c (16 May 1908), p.786; *The Times* (4 May 1908), p.13; Downes 1925, p.228; Charteris 1927, pp.204, 274; Mckibbin 1956, p.82; Mount 1969, p.431 (083)

Lent by the Carlton Club, London

Portraits of statesmen are notoriously dull, and at first sight Sargent's portrait of the eminent Tory Prime Minister, A. J. Balfour (1848–1930), does not look promising – impersonal setting, dark clothes, formalized pose and subdued colour scheme. What emerges on closer inspection, however, is a remarkably warm and living portrait of a man noted for his rectitude and reserve. Sargent accentuates the characteristics of his sitter in his usual witty fashion. The elegant, drooping, slightly dilettantish figure, standing on a Persian carpet, is made to look amazingly tall and slim. The large area of surrounding space adds to the impression of height. The figure, with one arm draped at right angles along the cornice, appears to conform to the pattern of grid lines established by the pillar, pilaster and panelling. Sargent had used this device before, in such notable works as *Lady Margaret Spicer* (1901; private collection) and *Lord Ribblesdale* (1902; Tate Gallery, London), but never in such an imposing design. Yet for all its formality, the pose is full of life. The ankles are crossed as if the figure were about to pirouette. Grasping his lapel in what was apparently a typical gesture, Balfour confronts his audience in a commanding attitude, his face full of intelligence and sensitivity. For what we have here is not simply a stereotyped image of a politician, but a complex and enigmatic personality.

Balfour had first made his mark as a metaphysician, publishing *A Defence of Philosophic Doubt* in 1879. He was an arbiter of elegance among the 'Souls', that coterie of supremely beautiful and cultivated aristocrats. Though cool and reserved by temperament he enjoyed enormous prestige in social and intellectual circles. His entry into politics was almost accidental, through the patronage of his uncle, the 3rd Marquess of Salisbury. His air of aristocratic and civilized aloofness hid a mind of great subtlety and penetration, and a strong grasp of practical politics. Balfour soon established his power in the party through the force of his intelligence and his personality, though he was never warmly liked and frequently misunderstood. He became Prime Minister on Salisbury's retirement in 1902, and for three years kept together an administration deeply divided over tariff reform and free trade. In the wartime coalition he was First Lord of the Admiralty, and later Foreign Secretary, playing a leading part in the peace negotiations.

Documents concerning the commission of this portrait have not come to light. It is not known why Sargent was selected, nor, in view of his unwillingness by this date to paint portraits, what pressure was put on him to accept. The picture had a mixed reception at the Academy, most reviewers preferring the companion portraits of the *Duke and Duchess of Connaught* (Royal Collection). The *Spectator*, however, praised the way in which character had been interpreted both in the face and the figure as a whole, and the artist's enormous ability in construction: 'The mastery of the whole thing is astonishing, and we ask ourselves could anyone else now place the figure so surely and so convincingly before us, and do so without having to resort to the arts of exaggeration'. G. K. Chesterton in the *Art Journal* (op.cit.) used the portrait as a peg for an extended piece on the state of politics and the mood of the time: 'By far the most important thing in the Exhibition, by the perspective of history, is Mr Sargent's portrait of Mr Balfour. And the trouble is that the type of its importance is not easy to explain, unless one realizes this great artist as a satirist of the *fin de siècle* . . . Mr Sargent's most sympathetic portrait is also one of his most sagacious . . . The portrait is not smiling, or in any way inclined to smile; it is not trying to wheedle friends and foes with mere amiability, as in the popular pictures of the man. It is the portrait of a philosopher and a statesman – a sad philosopher and a sad statesman. In its presence we feel the sober truths about the English governing class, its wide and ruinous scepticism, its remaining pillars of responsibility and reason . . . The tones of the picture are grave with grey and silver, as of the end of a day not wholly either of failure or victory, a day that leaves men fairly honourable and wholly disillusioned. Mr Sargent has left on canvas the record of what was worst at the end of the nineteenth century, after the death of Gladstone and the great crusades: the brazen fashion, the foul finance. Here, perhaps, he has left forever the record of what was best in it.'

52 *Henry James 1913*

Oil on canvas, 85 × 67.3 (33½ × 26½)

Signed and dated (top left and right): *John S. Sargent 1913*

Provenance: Presented to the sitter by a number of subscribers; bequeathed by him to the National Portrait Gallery, 1916

Exhibitions: R.A., 1914 (343); Panama-Pacific Exposition, San Francisco, 1915; Museum of Fine Arts, Boston, 1916; London 1926 (23), repr. 'Souvenir', p.82

Literature: *Athenaeum*, no.4514 (2 May 1914), p.631; *Graphic*, LXXXIX (9 May 1914), p.822; *Illustrated London News*, CXLIV (9 May 1914), p.770; *Nineteenth Century and After*, LXXV (June 1914), p.1317; *Spectator* (9 May 1914), p.11; *The Letters of Henry James*, ed. P. Lubbock, II (1920), pp.327–8, 330; Downes 1925, p.243; Charteris 1927, pp.161, 275; *Dictionary of National Biography* (1927), p.290; Jacques-Emile Blanche, *Portraits of a Lifetime* (1937), p.160; Mckibbin 1956, p.103; H. Montgomery Hyde, *Henry James at Home* (1969), pp.242–8, repr.; Mount 1969, pp.286, 442 (131), repr.; Ormond 1970, pp.66, 255–6, plate 108; Leon Edel, *Henry James: The Master* (1972), p. 488–95, repr.; Harry T. Moore, *Henry James and His World* (1974), p.111, repr. p.110 and cover (detail); Adeline R. Tintner, 'Sargent in the fiction of Henry James', *Apollo*, CII (August 1975), p.128, repr.

Lent by the National Portrait Gallery, London

This portrait was painted as a presentation to Henry James on his seventieth birthday by two hundred and sixty-nine subscribers. Edith Wharton had begun a subscription among the writer's American friends the previous year but this had been stopped on Henry James's express instructions. His English friends, however, raised over £500, and this sum was used to buy a reproduction

Charles II porringer and dish. Sargent, as an old friend, refused any remuneration for a portrait and the balance was used to commission a bust by a protégé of Sargent's, Derwent Wood (Tate Gallery, London). The picture was publicly willed to a national gallery in England, or, in default, to the Metropolitan Museum of Art, New York.

The portrait was completed after ten sittings during the early summer of 1913. After the third sitting James wrote: 'One is almost full-face, with one's left arm over the corner of one's chair-back and the hand brought round so that the thumb is caught in the arm hole of one's waistcoat, and said hand therefore, with the fingers a bit folded, entirely visible and "treated". Of course I'm sitting a little askance in the chair. The canvas comes down to where my watch chain (such as it is, poor thing!) is hung across the waistcoat, which latter, in itself, is found to be splendidly (poor thing though it be) and most interestingly treated. Sargent *can* make such things so interesting – such things as my coat-lappet and shoulder and sleeve too!' On 25 June 1913 he wrote: '... it is now finished, *parachevée* (I sat for the last time a couple of days ago); and is nothing less, evidently, than a very fine thing indeed, Sargent at his very best and poor old H.J. not at his worst; in short, a living breathing likeness and a masterpiece of painting. . . . I don't alas, exhibit a "point" in it, but am all large and luscious rotundity – by which you may see how true a thing it is. . . .'

In December the picture was put on exhibition for three days in Sargent's studio for the subscribers. On 18 December 1913, Henry James wrote: 'The exhibition of the Portrait came to a most brilliant end today, with a very great affluence of people . . . It has been a great and charming success – I mean the view has been; and the work itself acclaimed with an unanimity of admiration and, literally, of *intelligence*, that I can intimately testify to. For I really put myself on exhibition beside it, each of the days, morning and afternoon, and the translation (A perfect Omar Khayam, *quoi!*) visibly left the original nowhere'.

Most of James's friends admired the picture, but the critics at the 1914 Royal Academy were not universal in its praise, contrasting it with the enchanting *Countess of Rocksavage* (the Dowager Marchioness of Cholmondeley). Jacques-Emile Blanche complained that 'Of his model, so complex

52 *Henry James*

and finely shaded in his sensibility, he [Sargent] has made a business man from the provinces'. On the other hand Ezra Pound in his *Cantos* noted the sensitivity of the eyes, half closed as if in the middle of thought, but full of visual acuteness and the lips formed as if to speak, and the impression of authority. This latter quality is also brilliantly rendered in Sargent's full-length portrait of *The Earl of Wemyss and March* (1909; private collection).

While the picture was on exhibition at the Royal Academy it was vandalized by a militant suffragette, and despite repair its scars are visible. Sargent had made a small drawing of Henry James in 1886 (formerly James family), and another, secretly commissioned by Edith Wharton, in 1912 (Royal Collection).

Later Portrait Drawings and Charcoals

Fig.20 Drawing a head, c.1920

By the end of 1906 Sargent was declining most commissions for portraits, and by 1907 the embargo had become almost complete. In a very few cases he was badgered into changing his rule, but he did so most unwillingly. To those who still demanded to be depicted by the greatest portraitist of the age, he offered as an alternative his characteristic charcoal drawings. The rise in their number parallels the diminishing number of oils – about twelve charcoals in 1908, twenty in 1909, and over forty in 1910. A Sargent drawing became an important status symbol. 'How do you like your Sargent drawing?' was the conversational gambit of one distinguished diplomat to ladies he had never met before, and he claimed that it was successful nine times out of ten.

These charcoals, which Sargent produced in such large numbers for the last fifteen years of his life particularly, are one of his most characteristic forms of expression. Drawn in black charcoal, with the use of stump, on thick white Whatman paper, they are fluent, usually very like, and often brilliant. The handling is strong and decisive, very much that of a painter at work, and the head normally emerges from a series of straight or diagonal black strokes. The background is sometimes left white, but Sargent preferred a dark background, so that he could extract the maximum contrasts from his drawing, throwing the highlights of the head into strong relief. There is a wide variety of treatments, from the simple and sketchy to the elaborate and highly-finished. The bravura which distinguishes his oil portraits is no less evident in the drawings. The speed and vitality of his technique, the seizing and intensifying of essential characteristics, the immediate translation of the thing seen, are common to both. Although the drawings have an acute definition, this is rarely achieved by outline or purely linear emphasis, but through exactly calculated tonal relationships. Preoccupation with light continued to direct his vision.

When Sargent was in London or Boston, he usually spent the mornings doing charcoals, reserving the afternoons for his mural work. His fee, originally twenty-one guineas, rose to fifty around 1910, and in 1923 to one hundred, which was surprisingly modest. He usually required only one two-hour sitting, though he frequently destroyed what he had done and started again. There are a number of descriptions of what it was like to sit to Sargent. Hugo Charteris, one of the large Charteris clan who were some of Sargent's most consistent patrons, wrote in a letter of December 1910: 'To produce these straight lines, he lengthened my face, making it end at the top in a sort of point. He was very excited, but when he began to put in the collar and the bow-tie his long severe lines began to fade away. There was a lot of discussion, and finally he wiped out the collar and tie and drew me instead in an overcoat and evening scarf. The result is an eccentric costume and one which the inartistic mob will thoroughly disapprove of. However, he was once more delighted, and has more or less got his long, straight, severe lines. I look cynical, sly, severe, but very spry and alert . . . I believe I am already rather developing along the lines foreshadowed in the portrait'.

The influence of Sargent's charcoals has persisted down to the present day, particularly among society photographers.

53 *Alice Meynell*

53 *Alice Meynell 1894*

Pencil on white paper, 36.2 × 21 (14¼ × 8¼)

Inscribed and signed (lower right): *to Mr Coventry / Patmore / John S. Sargent*

Provenance: Coventry Patmore; the sitter; presented to the National Portrait Gallery by her husband, Wilfrid Meynell, 1928

Literature: repr. Meynell, 1903, 1927; repr. *Bookman*, Christmas supplement, 1921; *Review of Reviews* (January 1923), p.39; Viola Meynell, *Alice Meynell a Memoir* (1929), p.117, repr. facing p.118; D. Patmore, *Life and Times of Coventry Patmore* (1949), pp.218, 226; Mckibbin 1956, p.109

Lent by the National Portrait Gallery, London

Alice Meynell (1850–1922), the poetess, essayist and journalist. She was the daughter of T. J. Thompson and Christina Weller, both friends of Dickens, and the sister of Lady Butler, the painter of popular battle scenes. She became a Roman Catholic around 1872, and married Wilfrid Meynell in 1877. Besides bringing up a family of

54 *George Meredith*

eight children, she joined her husband in a remarkable journalistic partnership, writing prolifically herself, and helping him to edit magazines. Her first collection of poems was published in 1893 and at once established her reputation. She published several later volumes of poetry and essays. The elderly Coventry Patmore first met Alice Meynell in the early 1890s, and he was captivated by her beauty and charm. She was the last great passion of his life. Alice Meynell frequently accompanied him to Sargent's studio, while he was sitting for his portrait (no.39). It was at Patmore's request that Sargent executed the drawing of Mrs Meynell, which he gave to the poet. It is described by Osbert Burdett (Patmore, op.cit. p.218):

> We see a tall, slender figure, the stem, as it were, of a delicate refined face, a face a little weary, as if it were masked with the ashes of a fire which had wasted the spirit within. The distinction, the beauty is apparent, but there is the sense, often to be observed in an aristocratic face, of the end, of the weariness of a long road, most of which lies behind the traveller. The thread which binds the sheaf of Mrs Meynell's verse is a thread of sadness . . . Life is a burden to this poetess, not a joy. It imposes too great a strain upon her nerves.

When in 1903 Heinemann the publishers proposed publishing a book of reproductions of his work, Sargent suggested Alice Meynell as the author of the introductory essay. She wrote a perceptive if rather too generalized account of his painting, and Sargent was duly grateful: 'I am glad of the slight reserves and distinctions and oppositions which give to your essay the character of a study, in spite of its very high praise, and am honoured that such praise should come from you' (V. Meynell, op.cit. p.216). The two remained friendly, although a mutual barrier of shyness made their meetings uneasy.

54 *George Meredith 1896*

Charcoal on paper, 52.7 × 41.9 (20¾ × 16½)

Signed and dated (bottom right): *John S. Sargent / August 1896*

Provenance: In the same ownership since 1896

Exhibition: Either this or no. 55, Copley Hall, Boston, 1899 (100)

Literature: *Works of George Meredith*, I (1896), frontis.; S. Sassoon, *Meredith* (1948), p.217; L. Stevenson, *The Ordeal of George Meredith* (1954), pp.327–8, 329; Mckibbin 1956, p.109

Lent anonymously

One of two drawings of the ageing novelist George Meredith (1828–1909), executed during the summer of 1896. Sargent had first met Meredith sometime earlier, as a fellow guest at Ightham Mote, Kent, the home of General William Palmer and his wife. According to Stevenson, Meredith was persuaded to sit to Sargent by his friend and local MP, Sir Trevor Lawrence. The commission presumably resulted from the decision to include a portrait of the novelist in the 1896 edition of his *Works*.

Meredith was a reluctant sitter. In 1892 he declined to sit to G. F. Watts, telling Mrs Leslie Stephen that he had 'no ambition to provoke an English posterity's question, who is he? and my grizzled mug may be left to vanish' (*Letters*, ed. C. L. Cline, II, 1970, p.114). Eventually he relented, and the subdued profile portrait by Watts of 1893 in the National Portrait Gallery forms an interesting contrast to the much more forceful Sargent drawings.

Apparently referring to this drawing, Meredith wrote of his disgust at finding himself depicted as an old man: 'I beheld . . . a face of gruel in which floated balls like the eyes of a codfish kept for three days in ice. There were also brown concaves in the gruel. The nose was a reed shaken in the wind; the grim mouth was packed full of savage teeth – and this was an Impressionist impression of me. One eye was completely dead. Sargent made me an amicable Shade' (Stevenson, op.cit. p.328). In fact, as Stevenson noted, the drawing showed all 'the bristling vigor' of Meredith's 'defiant old age'. It is a much more direct and highly charged characterization than the Fitzwilliam drawing (no. 55).

55 *George Meredith 1896*

Charcoal on paper, 33 × 23 (13 × 9)

Signed and dated (lower right): *John S. Sargent / August 1896*

Provenance: Purchased by the Friends of the Fitzwilliam Museum from Captain George Meredith, 1944

Exhibitions: Either this or no.54, Copley

55 *George Meredith*

Hall, Boston, 1899 (100); London 1926 (445)

Literature: S. Sassoon, *Meredith* (1948), frontis.; Mckibbin 1956, p.109

Lent by the Syndics of the Fitzwilliam Museum, Cambridge

Drawn at the same time as no.54, apparently at Meredith's home, Flint Cottage, Box Hill, Surrey. It shows the novelist gazing upwards in a more idealized pose. Like the profile sketch of *Coventry Patmore* (no.40), it conveys the indomitable spirit and vision of the man of letters.

56 *William Rothenstein 1897*

Lithograph on paper, 68.6 × 50.8 (27 × 20)

Provenance: Given to the British Museum by the artist

Literature: *Print Collector's Quarterly*, XIII (1926), pp.35, 45, plate 3; William Rothenstein, *Men and Memories* (1931), p.304; Mckibbin 1956, p.120; Mount 1969, p.206; Ormond 1970, p.249

Lent by the Trustees of the British Museum

William Rothenstein was the well-known English painter and friend of Sargent. This lithograph was made while Rothenstein was drawing Sargent in 1897 (and later published as a lithograph in Rothenstein's

56 William Rothenstein

English Portraits, 1897). The circumstances were recalled in Rothenstein's *Men and Memories*: 'While I was drawing Sargent he couldn't bear to remain idle; he puffed and fumed, and directly I had done, he insisted on my sitting to him. He made a drawing on transfer paper, which was laid down on the stone by Goulding, six proofs only being pulled. One of these Sargent gave to Helleu, who asked for it, one went to the Print Room of the British Museum and two he gave to me'.

Sargent made only six lithographs throughout his career. These are discussed by Albert Belleroche in the *Print Collector's Quarterly*, XIII (1926).

57 *Gabriel Fauré 1898*

Charcoal and pencil on paper, 18.7 × 24.4 (7⅜ × 5⅝)

Signed, dated and inscribed (upper right): *John S. Sargent / the Hut / June 26 98 / To Frank Schuster*

Provenance: Given by the artist to Frank Schuster; Mrs Stuart Wortley (later Lady Stuart of Wortley); The Hon Clare Stuart Wortley; by descent to the present owner

Exhibition: Claridge Gallery, London, 1925 (19)

Literature: *The Times* (2 July 1925), p.9; Mckibbin 1956, p.95

Lent by Robert A. Cecil
Exhibited Leeds and London only

Gabriel Fauré, the French composer. Sargent was an ardent admirer of the music of Fauré and the two were close friends for nearly thirty years. According to Percy Grainger: 'For many years (longer than I knew him) he [Sargent] had been the apostle of Gabriel Fauré in England, bringing over that great composer to London for public and private performances of his compositions, arranging performances of Fauré's works by the Cappe Quartet, Leon Delafosse, and other exquisite artists and the like. In my opinion Sargent is chiefly responsible for the fine understanding of Fauré's music that obtains in England'. (Charteris 1927, p.150).

In June 1898 Fauré came to London to conduct his incidental music to Maeterlinck's play *Pelleas and Melisande*. The strong cast included Mrs Patrick Campbell and Martin-Harvey in the title roles with Forbes-Robertson as Golaud. The particular quality of 'remoteness and archaic simplicity' had been achieved in the Paris production by special lighting effects, and it was hoped that the same impression would be produced in London through the incidental music. However, the critic in *The Times* wrote: 'Judged by the ordinary standards of theatrical music, which are perhaps higher in the present day in England than anywhere else, it is scarcely satisfactory, being wanting alike in charm and in dramatic power. It has, indeed, the vagueness of melodic and harmonious progression which may be held to suit best the character of the play, but its continued absence of tangible form, not to speak of its actual ugliness at many points, is such as to disturb rather than assist the illusion of the scene. In fact it is the least successful feature in a production of great if somewhat fantastic beauty and pathos . . . the piece was received with much enthusiasm although one or two passages occasioned some merriment among those to whom the *naïvetés* of Maeterlinck were new'.

The following week-end a house-party forgathered at the home of the impressario Frank Schuster, 'The Hut' at Bray. It included Fauré, Sargent, Mrs Stuart Wortley, Mrs Patrick Campbell, and Sarah Bernhardt, who was in London performing for a short season at the Lyric Theatre (Mrs Patrick Campbell and Sarah Bernhardt were to perform together in *Pelleas and*

Melisande in 1905). Sargent evidently seized the opportunity to make this sketch, and also another of Fauré in full-face, looking downwards, with Mrs Patrick Campbell looking over his shoulder (untraced). The charm of this drawing lies in the nonchalance of the attitude of the sitter, who is possibly even asleep.

Sargent evidently considered Fauré's profile to be his strongest feature. Apart from the untraced sketch already mentioned, both the oil (1896; Fauré-Frémiet collection) and another drawing (1896; Fogg Art Museum, Cambridge, Mass.) show the composer in near profile.

58 *Harley Granville-Barker 1900*

Charcoal on paper, 61.6 × 47.7 (24¼ × 18¾)

Signed and dated (bottom right): *John S. Sargent 1900*

Provenance: Offered to the National Portrait Gallery by George Bernard Shaw, 1944; held by the Wakefield Trust until 1960, when it entered the collection

Exhibition: London 1926 (454)

Literature: Mckibbin 1956, p.83 (misdated 1909)

Lent by the National Portrait Gallery, London

Granville-Barker (1877–1946), the actor, producer, dramatist and critic. He helped to transform the British theatrical scene with his series of radical productions of modern plays at the Royal Court Theatre. He himself wrote a number of highly acclaimed plays, notable for their power of characterization and their sharp social criticism, including *The Voysey Inheritance* and *The Madras House*. In later life Barker withdrew from the theatre, under the influence of his second wife, although he continued to lecture and write about it.

It is not known if this drawing was a commission from Shaw, or, if it was not, how he came to acquire it. It was drawn shortly before the period of their closest association, when Barker was producing Shaw's work at the Royal Court. The drawing is a tribute to Barker's youth and extreme good looks, but it does not perhaps convey his drive, energy and high spirits. The squiggle under the last numeral of the inscribed date has sometimes been misread as a '9'.

59 *Ethel Smyth 1901*

Black chalk on paper, 59.8 × 46 (23½ × 18⅛)

Inscribed and signed (top left): *to Mrs Hunter John S. Sargent*

Provenance: Mrs Charles Hunter, the sister of the sitter; given to the National Portrait Gallery by her daughters, Mrs Elwes, Mrs Williamson and Lady Grant Lawson, 1944

Exhibitions: Pastel Society, 1907 (187); Royal Society of Portrait Painters, Grafton Galleries, London, 1916 (43); London 1926 (474), repr. 'Souvenir', p.42

Literature: Charteris 1927, p.152; Ethel Smyth, *What Happened Next* (1940), pp.194–5; Mckibbin 1956, pp.123–4; C. Marshall (C. St John), *Ethel Smyth* (1959), pp.78, 99, 251, repr. facing p.96; Ormond 1970, p.251, plate 88

Lent by the National Portrait Gallery, London

Ethel Smyth, later Dame Ethel Smyth (1858–1944), the composer, author and feminist. The daughter of a British general, she took up a musical career in the face of parental opposition, studied at Leipzig, and gradually established her reputation as a composer of operas, oratorios and concertos. Her best known work is *The Wreckers* (1906), with a libretto by her close friend Henry Brewster. Apart from her musical interests, Ethel Smyth was a vociferous and intrepid champion of women's rights, and she played a prominent part in the suffragette movement. She was a wholly original character, self-opinionated, domineering and vivid, mannish in appearance and prone to intense relationships with women.

Sargent was the intimate friend of Ethel Smyth's sister, Mrs Charles Hunter, the wife of a coalmine owner, a great hostess and a keen patroness of the arts. So close was Sargent to this worldly and ebullient woman that gossip said she was his mistress. She had sat for her own portrait to Sargent in 1898, and her three daughters, who gave this drawing, were painted in a graceful group in 1902, *The Misses Hunter* (both Tate Gallery, London). Sargent's relationship with Ethel Smyth was less easy. He was irritated by her strident feminism, but he remained an admirer of her music, and endured the discomforts of her cottage as a guest. When Sargent heard that she had given up smoking, he expostulated: 'Well, I

57 *Gabriel Fauré*

never should have thought you were so weakminded!' There are many references to the artist in Ethel Smyth's innumerable volumes of autobiography. In *What Happened Next* (op.cit.) she describes the story of this drawing, which was executed at her cottage, One Oak in Surrey: '... in December [1901] Sargent carried out his intention of doing a charcoal drawing of me seated at the piano and singing. All the time he kept on imploring me to sing the most desperately exciting songs I knew, such as Schubert's "Gruppe aus Tartarus", Holmès's "Chanson des Gas d'Irlande", and so on, crying out, as he hastily made dab after dab at his canvas: "What's that? ... *What's that?*" It took him only just over one and a half hours to draw what according to some of his colleagues – Charles Furse among the number – is one of the most remarkable *singing* portraits extant.

'He himself was rather perturbed about it, because when his servant first caught sight of it, he gave a little jump and said: "Oh sir! is that lady mad?"; but it reassured him to hear that on seeing the drawing one of my nephews remarked: "Fancy his having done Aunt Ethel biking and catching flies!" He himself always referred to that drawing as "The Seagull".' Earlier Sargent had been

58 *Harley Granville-Barker*

asked by Brewster to paint a head of her, 'and they say he wants her in a calm mood. Miss Smyth in a calm mood!' (Charteris 1927).

Sargent's admiration for Ethel Smyth's gifts as a singer was shared by many others, among them Maurice Baring (*The Puppet Show of Memory*, 1922, p.140); 'the rare and exquisite quality and delicacy of her voice, the strange thrill and wail, the distinction and distinct clear utterance, where every word and every note told without effort, and the whirlwind of passion and feeling she evoked in a song such as "Come o'er the Sea" or Brahms' "Botschaft".'

60 *Mrs Sackville-West 1905*
(later Lady Sackville)

Charcoal on paper, 61 × 45.7 (24 × 18)

Inscribed, dated and signed (bottom right): *to my friend Mrs Sackville West / for Vita's birthday 1905 / John S. Sargent*

Provenance: By family descent

Literature: Mckibbin 1956, p.121; Harold Nicolson, *Diaries and Letters 1930–1939*, ed. Nigel Nicolson (1966), repr. facing p.20; Susan Mary Alsop, *Lady Sackville* (1978), p.147 (repr. cover of New York edition)

Lent by Nigel Nicolson

Mrs Sackville-West was the natural daughter of Lionel Sackville-West and the dancer 'Pepita' Duran. At the age of nineteen she was permitted to join her father, who was Minister in Washington, and become his hostess. She later married her cousin, Lionel Sackville-West, and became châtelaine of Knole. She was a well-known figure in social circles and became the centre of a sensational court case when she inherited a large legacy and the priceless art collection in the Paris apartment of Sir John Murray Scott, who had in turn received this from Sir Richard Wallace. Sir John's family alleged that she had exerted 'undue influence' over him, but Lady Sackville won the case. Her biography was first written by her daughter, Vita Sackville-West, in *Pepita* (1937), and recently by Susan Mary Alsop, *Lady Sackville* (1978).

Lady Sackville's unpublished *Diaries* reveal that she sat to Sargent for a portrait in oils but it was a failure. Her notes are very revealing for the light they throw on a subject's response to sitting to the artist. On 21 January 1905 she wrote: 'My sittings

59 *Ethel Smyth*

with Sargent are quite pleasant, as he is very *sympathique*, and talks well and all the time. I am done in a simple black dress and a lovely scarf and I wear some of my fine emeralds. I go 4 times a week and sit over 2 hours. He wants to do it with my mouth slightly open, but I don't like that.' Just over a week later, on 30 January, she wrote: 'My picture is not progressing favourably. I have bought a little lace coat at Lucile, which Sargent likes very much so I am wearing it in the picture. He says he cannot catch that 'fleeting' expression there is in my eyes, my expression is changing all the time'. She went up to London again on 6 February, and on 11 February wrote in her diary: 'Sargent had painted a lovely head of me but has scratched it all out again. He said the painting was not good enough for him to sign. He began again and made a horrid face and he was not pleased when I told him I did not like it at all! But he wrote afterwards that he would do a drawing of me for Vita's birthday, for nothing! as *amende honorable*.' On 18 February she wrote that she had sat four times to Sargent that week, and on 21 February: 'Sargent did a charming drawing of me which I will give Vita for her birthday. It took him an hour to do it, and he played the piano beautifully for me while resting.' Five days later: 'Sargent has sent me the drawing, framed, and has written on it: "To my friend, Mrs S. West, for Vita's birthday 1905" and signed it. Tio [her husband, Lionel Sackville-West, later Lord Sackville] likes it very much and so does Vita. Seery [Sir John Murray Scott] and Vita do not like my portrait very much. They say it may be Sargent's José [nickname for herself] but it is not quite *their* José!' Evidently the project for the commissioned oil was not yet abandoned. On 1 March she again wrote: 'I went to Sargent yesterday and again this morning, thinking he would be away and took Vita and Seery. But Sargent was waiting for me and begged me to take off my hat and redid my face; he made me look away and I much preferred when he made me look straight at one. Tio said I was not very vain to look dishevelled'. The last mention of the portrait occurs one week later, on 8 March: 'Went to Sargent's again and Tio liked it again, although he re-did my face a sixth time. Dress is not yet finished.' After this Lady Sackville went to Paris and Monte Carlo and there are no further references to the painting.

The unfinished oil has not survived and

60 *Mrs Sackville-West*

61 *Lady Helen Vincent*

was probably destroyed by the artist. The drawing would seem to be to Lady Sackville's specifications, for the sitter is indeed looking straight at the spectator, possibly wearing some of her 'fine emeralds' and a little lace coat.

61 *Lady Helen Vincent* c.*1905*
(later Viscountess d'Abernon)

Charcoal on paper, 61 × 45.7 (24 × 18)

Provenance: Bequeathed to York City Art Gallery by Viscountess d'Abernon

Literature: Charteris 1925, repr. facing p.124; Viscountess d'Abernon, *Red Cross and Berlin Embassy 1915–1926* (1946), frontis.; Mckibbin 1956, p.91

Lent by York City Art Gallery

Lady Helen Vincent, née Helen Duncombe, was the daughter of the 1st Earl of Feversham. She married the financier and diplomat Sir Edgar Vincent, later created Viscount d'Abernon, ambassador to Berlin from 1920 to 1926.

Lady Helen was one of the great beauties of her day and she and her husband lived at Esher Place, where they assembled a large art collection. Sargent painted a three-quarter-length portrait of her in Venice in 1904 (private collection) which is closely related to this drawing.

to my friend Mrs Swinton
John S. Sargent 1906

62 *Mrs George Swinton*

62 *Mrs George Swinton 1906*

Charcoal on paper, 61×47.6 ($24 \times 18\frac{3}{4}$)

Inscribed, signed and dated (bottom right):
to my friend Mrs Swinton / *John S. Sargent 1906*

Provenance: By family descent

Exhibition: Pastel Society, London, 1907
(190)

Literature: *The Times* (13 June 1907), p.4;
Mckibbin 1956, p.125; Mount 1969,
pp.267–8

Lent by Major-General John Swinton, OBE

Sargent remained on friendly terms with
the Swintons for twenty years (see no. 42).
They attended numerous musical parties,
and Sargent was a great admirer of Mrs
Swinton's singing voice. In 1906 she decided
to become a professional singer, and
Sargent was approached to make a charcoal
drawing. On 17 May 1906 he wrote back,
rather flirtatiously: 'I will be delighted to do
a black and white sketch of you to be
reproduced for your nefarious purposes
whatever they are. It is a thing I have
wanted to do, in fact asked you to let me do,
so please consider it as an offering handed to
you across the footlights, delicious sensation!
in a large bouquet with enormous ribbons.
I have a free morning tomorrow Friday.
Would you come at 11 with your throat
bared to the winds? or Monday morning?'.

Mrs Swinton's first public concert was
held a few days later on 22 May at the
Aeolian Hall and was a great success. She
sang French and Russian songs, as well as
works by Gluck, Schubert and Fauré.
Percy Grainger also played arrangements
after Bach and Chopin. *The Times* ap-
plauded her debut, attributing the fact that
'she showed a tendency to sing a shade
sharp' to her nervousness. Sargent was there
and wrote two days later: 'You were
(further concealment is useless) a huge
success, and showed so many qualities that
one must lump a great many different
compliments into one. I stopped at the
framemakers to hurry them up about your
drawing, and he says he sent it yesterday . . .
Best to have it photographed one third of the
size – *not* the whole size of the original – it
would look colossal'.

63 *Viola Tree*

63 *Viola Tree 1907*

Charcoal on paper, 61 × 48.3 (24 × 19)

Signed and dated (top left and right):
John S. Sargent 1907

Provenance: The sitter; by descent to her
son

Exhibitions: New Gallery, London, 1909
(160); London 1926 (443); York Art
Gallery, 1926 (83)

Literature: Max Beerbohm, *Herbert
Beerbohm Tree* (1921), repr. facing p.143;
Viola Tree, *Castles in the Air* (1926), p.260;
Mckibbin 1956, p.127

Lent by David Tree Parsons

Viola Tree (1884–1938), daughter of the
actor-manager Sir Herbert Beerbohm Tree,
and herself a singer of some distinction.
She was beautiful, high-spirited and much
loved. Tree was devoted to her and wept
copiously at her marriage in 1912 to the
drama critic, Alan Parsons. Music was
probably the link between her and Sargent,
who was a friend. He presented Viola with
the charcoal portrait of her father (no.64),
which was probably drawn at the same
period as this vivacious charcoal of her.
The artist told her it was 'one of his favour-
ites, and he had it photographed for his own
private collection.' Either this, or another
second charcoal portrait of Viola (also
dated 1907), was included in a sale at
Christie's, 19 December 1919 (lot 53).

64 *Sir Herbert Beerbohm Tree*
c.*1907*

Charcoal on paper, 61.5 × 47.5 (24¼ × 18¾)

Inscribed and signed (lower right): *to Miss
Viola Tree / from her friend / John S. Sargent*

Provenance: By family descent

Exhibitions: London 1926 (512), repr.
'Souvenir', p.114; York Art Gallery, 1926
(64)

Literature: Max Beerbohm, *Herbert
Beerbohm Tree* (1921), pp.177–8, repr.
facing p.178; Viola Tree, *Castles in the Air*
(1926), p.260; Mckibbin 1956, p.127

Lent by Denys Parsons

Sir Herbert Beerbohm Tree (1853–1917),
the successful actor-manager, and the half-
brother of Max Beerbohm. He first made
his name as a comedian and character
actor, but in later life aspired to grander and

64 *Sir Herbert Beerbohm Tree*

Colour plate XIII *A Spanish Interior c.1903* (no.82)

Colour plate XIV *A Siesta c. 1907–8* (no. 85)

more tragic parts. His popular productions at Her Majesty's Theatre, ranging from Shakespeare to Shaw, were noted for their lavishness of presentation. Tree possessed boundless enthusiasm and vitality, one of those figures who appear larger than life. Sargent's drawing of him is vividly alive, catching him with his mouth open, gazing intently upwards, his eyeballs protruding. Like the portrait sketches of Patmore and Meredith (nos.40 and 55), the drawing has an inspirational force, that conveys not only a telling likeness but a sense of the actor's creative springs.

The drawing was given to Tree's daughter, Viola (no.63). She described him sitting (Beerbohm, op.cit. p.178): 'The moment he had stepped on to the daïs, I said to him: "Look towards the window, Daddy". He did so. Mr Sargent became covered with confusion. "Don't strain, don't strain; you will never be able to keep that pose." My father seemed surprised, and answered: "No, no, it's quite natural." This defiant turn of the head and illuminated look was normal to him, before whose mind's-eye processions of popes, jugglers, and sinister servants holding peacocks in the leash passed continuously to the accompaniment of music, sad, strange, or grotesque. His most beautiful production, *Herod*, was probably built up like this, while he was driving through the streets, or carrying on a polite conversation.'

65 *The Baroness de Meyer* c.*1907*

Charcoal on paper, 87.6 × 71 (34½ × 28)

Signed (bottom right): *John S. Sargent*

Provenance: The Hon Clare Stuart Wortley; presented to Birmingham City Art Gallery by the National Art-Collections Fund, 1945

Exhibitions: *Fair Women*, New Gallery, London, 1908 (155); London 1926 (538); Birmingham 1964 (92)

Literature: *Illustrated London News*, CXXII (7 March 1908), repr. p.342; Mckibbin 1956, p.92 (dated 1907); *Saturday Book*, XXV (1965), repr. p.28; Ormond 1970, pp.67, 251, plate 89

Lent by Birmingham City Museums and Art Gallery

Olga, Baroness de Meyer (1872?–1929), daughter of the Italian Duke of Caracciolo and his wife Blanche Sampayo. She was the

65 *The Baroness de Meyer*

goddaughter of Edward VII (reputedly her father), and from an early age moved in a smart cosmopolitan set. While still a girl her beauty attracted many artists, and she sat to Whistler, Boldini, Helleu and Conder. In 1892 she married the much older Prince de Brancaccio, and in 1899, after the break-up of her first marriage, Adolph de Meyer, the portrait and fashion photographer. He was born in Paris of obscure parentage and was made a baron by the King of Saxony, apparently at the instigation of Edward VII. The De Meyers had beauty, talent and a thirst for social life, and they were in the forefront of fashionable society before and after the First World War; for further biographical details see P. Julian, *De Meyer* (1976).

Sargent's drawing was done either in London or Venice, where the De Meyers rented a palace every autumn. They had many friends in common. The drawing of the baroness is a splendid piece of flamboyant draughtsmanship, the sweeping lines of the hat and dress acting as a frame for the elegant, aristocratic head. The characterization is not entirely sympathetic, and it is interesting to compare this drawing with De Meyer's soft and tender photographs of his wife, which suggest a much more vulnerable personality.

66 *Edward VII on his Death-bed* 1910

Charcoal on paper, 44.8 × 58.8 (17$\frac{5}{8}$ × 23$\frac{1}{8}$)

Signed and dated (top left and right): *John S. Sargent May 8th 1910*

Provenance: Commissioned for the Royal Collection

Literature: Mckibbin 1956, p.94; R. L. Ormond, *Face of Monarchy* (1977), p.197, plate 141

Lent by Her Majesty Queen Elizabeth II

Edward VII died shortly before midnight on 6 May 1910. The circumstances in which Sargent came to be asked to draw the dead king two days later are not known. Perhaps a sense of lost opportunity dictated the choice, for Edward was the one great Edwardian figure whom Sargent had never painted. In 1901 he declined the commission for the official coronation picture, giving as his reasons the fact that his 'entire responsibility on nature both for likeness and for qualities of painting' made him 'par-

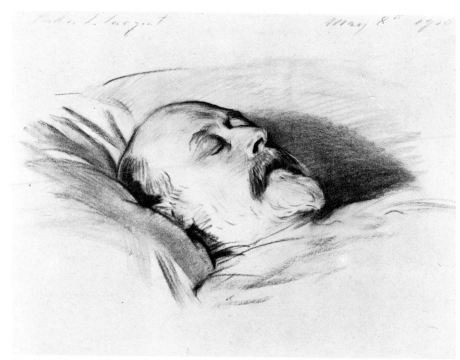

66 *Edward VII on his Death-bed*

67 *The Two Girls*

ticularly unfit for this high task'. In 1907 Edward VII recommended Sargent for a knighthood, together with three other artists, describing him in a note to Sir Henry Campbell-Bannerman as 'the most distinguished portrait painter in England' (extracts from letters in the Royal Archives, Windsor, kindly communicated by Miss Jane Langton). Sargent, however, was unwilling to relinquish his American citizenship, and he declined the honour. The drawing of Edward was not Sargent's only depiction of a dead sitter. In 1908 he made a very similar death-bed drawing of Ethel Smyth's close friend and collaborator, Harry Brewster.

67 *The Two Girls 1911*

Charcoal on paper, 39.4 × 49.5 ($15\frac{1}{2}$ × $19\frac{1}{2}$)

Inscribed and signed (bottom right): *to Violet – John S. Sargent*

Provenance: Given by the artist to his sister, Violet Ormond; thence by family descent

Exhibitions: London 1926 (264); Tate Gallery 1926, cat. 8; Birmingham 1964 (94)

Literature: Mckibbin 1956, p.114

Lent by the Ormond Family

According to the Sargent Trust list (Ormond family, 'Drawings' no.3) this drawing of Rose-Marie Ormond and Polly Barnard wrapped in the same Cashmere shawl was executed at the Simplon in 1911. Like the water-colours of this period, though in a more formal and restrained style, the drawing explores the decorative possibilities of two gracefully posed female figures. Their ballooning dresses form the base of an elegant pyramidal design. The Ormond and Barnard sisters were often referred to as the 'intertwingles' because of their easy exchange of poses.

68 *Lord Buckhurst 1912*
(later 9th Earl De La Warr)

Charcoal on paper, 61 × 48 (24 × 18)

Signed and dated (bottom right): *John S. Sargent 1912*

Provenance: By family descent

Literature: Mckibbin 1956, p.92

Lent anonymously

68 *Lord Buckhurst*

Lord Buckhurst was born in 1900 and later had a distinguished parliamentary career.

Sargent's drawings of boys are relatively few compared with his prodigious output of women and girls. In this engaging sketch he has broken with his often predictable formula of *hauteur* and flattery. The subject looks directly at the spectator and there is a suggestion that he is wearing a heavy flannel shirt in the way that the open collar falls from the neck.

69 *Mary Anderson* (*Mrs A. F. de Navarro*) *1913*

Charcoal on paper, 60.5 × 48 (23¾ × 18⅞)

Signed and dated (bottom left and right): *John S. Sargent 1913*

Provenance: By family descent

Exhibition: Birmingham 1964 (93)

Literature: Mary Anderson, *A Few More Memories* (1936), frontis; Mckibbin 1956, p.82

Lent by J. M. de Navarro
Exhibited Leeds and London only

Mary Anderson (1859–1940), the celebrated American actress. She first appeared on stage as Juliet in 1875, and soon established an international reputation. She played at the Lyceum Theatre in London during the absences of Henry Irving in America, and was acclaimed both for her beauty and her dramatic talent. She left the stage in 1889 and married Antonio de Navarro the following year, settling down in the Cotswold village of Broadway. She and Sargent were old friends.

70 *Daisy, Princess of Pless 1912*

Charcoal on paper, 59.7 × 47 (23½ × 18½)

Signed (bottom right): *John S. Sargent*

Provenance: The sitter; Constance, Duchess of Westminster

Literature: *Daisy Princess of Pless by Herself*, ed. Major Desmond Chapman-Huston (1928), frontis.; Mckibbin 1956, p.116

Lent by W. John Koch

The Princess of Pless, née Mary ('Daisy') Cornwallis-West, was one of the most dazzling personalities of the Edwardian age. After her first season she was married to the enormously wealthy Prince Henry of Pless,

69 *Mary Anderson*

who succeeded his father as the quasi-autonomous ruler of Furstenstein and Pless in 1907. Despite the immensely stiff etiquette of the Imperial German court, the princess maintained her natural vivacity and charm and moved with ease both among the nobility and *nouveaux riches* of Europe and America. Her own subjects held her in affection. During the First World War she worked in the Berlin War Hospital and for the British prisoners-of-war. Her memoirs, *Daisy of Pless* (1928), *From my Private Diary* (1931), and *What I left Unsaid* (1936), are a candid and amusing account of her life.

Sargent has captured her natural ebullience and physical beauty, and there is a reference to the famous 'Pless pearls' (over seven feet in length) which fall from her elongated neck. It is possible that the drawing was commissioned in order that it could be reproduced in photographic form and distributed as gifts. One of these is reproduced as the frontispiece of the first volume of her memoirs and signed by her.

A full biography of the princess is in preparation by the present owner of this drawing.

71 *Lady Ritchie 1914*

Charcoal on paper, $61.5 \times 49.5 \ (24\frac{1}{2} \times 19\frac{1}{2})$

Signed and dated (bottom left and right):
John S. Sargent 1914

Provenance: By family descent to the sitter's granddaughter

Exhibitions: Royal Society of Portrait Painters, London, 1916 (21); London 1926 (483), repr. 'Souvenir', p.109

Literature: *Letters of Anne Thackeray Ritchie*, ed. H. Ritchie (1924), pp.282–7, frontis.; Mckibbin 1956, p.119; Ormond 1970, p.256 plate 111

Lent by Mrs Edward Norman-Butler

Anne Thackeray Ritchie (1837–1919), the eldest daughter of W. M. Thackeray the novelist, the wife of Sir Richmond Ritchie, and a considerable author and personality in her own right. She was warm-hearted, imaginative, impulsive and amusing, with a gift for friendship and a wide circle of admirers. She knew everyone in the literary world, and her own novels and essays were considered highly at the time. She also wrote various books of reminiscences which are of interest today for the light they throw on the late Victorian period.

70 *Daisy, Princess of Pless*

Sargent's drawing of Lady Ritchie was commissioned by more than a hundred of her friends, and presented to her in August 1914 with a silver inkstand and a pair of candlesticks. Henry James wrote to her on 30 June 1914: 'It is altogether delightful to think that this happy thought of your likeness being "took" by our all responsive and all-ready Sargent is on the way to be effectively arranged, for such a Public Treasure shall the work appear destined to become, if all goes well with it'. Lady Ritchie herself described the sittings in letters of 9 and 30 July to Mrs George Prothero and Rhoda Broughton. In the first she wrote: 'I have just come away from Sargent's studio. It is the most lovely, *fine* picture – I can't tell you how I have loved the gift, the givers and the devisers, or how I have enjoyed the sittings. I could only tell Mr Sargent that when I came away, the picture itself would – could thank him for me'. And in the second: 'It really is an enchanting picture. I am more touched and interested and grateful than ever. I went for another sitting yesterday and he said I like your bonnet too much, may I add it? and so my poke bonnet is there supreme . . . I feel quite shy before my portrait it is so *human*, and I feel so like it, yet more grim alas!'

72 *Lady Diana Manners 1914*
(now Lady Diana Cooper)

Charcoal on paper, 59.7 × 47 (23½ × 18½)

Signed and dated (bottom left and right): *John S. Sargent 1914*

Provenance: Violet, Duchess of Rutland; the sitter

Exhibition: London 1926 (526), repr. 'Souvenir', p.108

Literature: Mckibbin 1956, p.108; Lady Diana Cooper, *The Rainbow Comes and Goes* (1958), p.68

Lent by Lady Diana Cooper

Lady Diana's eventful life has been recounted in her three volumes of autobiography, *The Rainbow Comes and Goes* (1958), *The Light of Common Day* (1959), and *Trumpets from the Steep* (1960). During the 1914–18 War she served as a nurse at Guy's Hospital. She took the leading part in Max Reinhardt's spectacular production of *The Miracle*, which ran intermittently for twelve years in England, the United States and on

71 *Lady Ritchie*

the Continent. She married the writer and statesman, Duff Cooper (later created Viscount Norwich), and was first ambassadress to France after the 1939–45 War.

Lady Diana well remembers sitting for this charcoal, which took no more than an hour or two. She remembers Sargent dashing backwards and forwards at the paper uttering strange incomprehensible noises.

73 Mrs Adrian Stokes 1914

Pencil on paper, 35 × 24.5 (13¾ × 9⅝)

Inscribed, signed and dated (bottom right): *to my friend Mrs Adrian Stokes / John S. Sargent / St Lorenzen Nov 1914*

Provenance: By family descent

Exhibition: London 1926 (249)

Literature: Mckibbin 1956, p.124

Lent by Mrs Antony Sefi

Mrs Adrian Stokes, née Marianne Preindlsberger, was a gifted artist who painted biblical and genre subjects. She was born in Austria, studied art in Munich and met her husband, the landscape painter, in France. She used gesso and tempera in her works and a technique known as 'Schoenfield's tempera', which gave the appearance of fresco on a rough plaster ground. Her exhibited pictures bore such titles as *Saint Elizabeth spinning for the poor* and *Primavera*. An interesting memoir of Sargent is contained in an article by her husband, Adrian Stokes: 'John Singer Sargent', *The Old Water-Colour Society's Club 1925–1926*, third annual volume, pp.51–65.

It was while Sargent was in their company, in August 1914, that war broke out. Sargent had set out to join them with Colonel Armstrong at Seisser Alpenhaus, in the Dolomites, late in July 1914. Colonel Armstrong was arrested and the party's pictures were impounded by the authorities. They were refused permission to leave the country, and settled down at the Capella Inn, Colfuschg, but continued to paint. Although there were occasional interruptions by drunken troops, 'Sargent's equanimity was disturbed by none of these things. He never grumbled, he never complained, but went out to work with what materials had been left to him . . . He seemed to regard the whole affair simply as an example of human folly.' (Stokes, op.cit. p.58.) It was only after the death of

72 *Lady Diana Manners*

73 *Mrs Adrian Stokes*

74 *Angela McInnes*

the husband of his favourite niece, Rose-Marie, that he realized the implications of the war.

The party moved on to St Lorenzen in the Pusterthal valley (near the present Austro-Italian border), to stay with Sargent's old friend Carl Maldoner 'who is a perfect brick', and continued to make painting expeditions. Sargent's landscapes at this time have an atmosphere of foreboding and often include religious imagery. Finally, the Stokeses were permitted to travel to London: 'Sargent's recommendation had procured a passport for me, through the American Ambassador in Vienna; but, though he wrote repeatedly, none came for himself. He sent his servant on with luggage, expecting soon to follow. But day after day the anxiously awaited post failed to bring the passport; so he decided to undertake a long journey to Vienna and enquire, why? It was night when he left St Lorenzen. My last impression of him, in those war days, was a large tall figure, in long dark cloak, hurriedly bidding good-bye to a landlady in the sombre arch below her inn, and partially lit by the stable lantern she carried. In his hand he held a bundle of banknotes fluttering in the wind. Some, indeed, quite unheeded by him, were blown away'. (Stokes, op.cit. p.59.) By the first week of December Sargent was back in London.

Sargent's sketch of Mrs Adrian Stokes, made during their anxious time at St Lorenzen, is again in contrast to his commissioned charcoals. Her kindly features are brilliantly captured and she has a sympathetic smile and charming eyes. They remained close friends and were both avid chess players.

74 *Angela McInnes* 1915
(later Angela Thirkell)

Charcoal on paper, 63.5 × 43.2 (25 × 17) (cut down)

Provenance: By family descent

Literature: Mckibbin 1956, p.126; Margot Strickland, *Angela Thirkell: Portrait of a Lady Novelist* (1977), p.33, plate 14

Lent by Simon McInnes

Angela McInnes, later Angela Thirkell, the novelist. She was the daughter of J. W. Mackail, OM, and Margaret Burne-Jones. Her novels of English life in the tradition of Jane Austen and Trollope enjoyed success throughout the English-speaking world.

According to the sitter's recent biographer, this sensitive drawing was considered a great success: 'Everybody remarked upon it. He [Sargent] had exactly captured Angela's pride and vulnerability: her swan neck was elongated, her mouth tremulous; there was a fierce gaze in her eyes'. Henry James was asked to come and see it and replied: 'I will, with pleasure, undertake to be in some sort of condition to come to you at 5'. His comments on the drawing have not survived.

75 *Henry Tonks* 1918

Pencil and ink on paper, 24.8 × 37.1 (9¾ × 14⅝)

Inscribed (upper right): *H.Q. Guards Division / Aug. 4th 1918 / to my friend Henry Tonks / John S. Sargent*

Provenance: Henry Tonks; given to the Fitzwilliam Museum by the Friends of the Fitzwilliam, 1937

Literature: Mckibbin 1956, p.126

Lent by the Syndics of the Fitzwilliam Museum, Cambridge

Henry Tonks (1862–1937) trained as a doctor and became a successful anatomist. He studied art under Frederick Brown at the Westminster School of Art, and when the latter was appointed Slade Professor of Fine Art at University College, London, Tonks abandoned his medical career to become Brown's assistant. Between them they brought a new emphasis to fine draughtsmanship and were highly influential among the rising artists of the time, particularly Augustus John and William Orpen. In painting they advocated impressionism and were aided by Steer who also taught at the Slade School. In 1895 Tonks was elected to the New English Art Club and in 1917 he succeeded Brown as professor until his retirement in 1930.

Sargent and Tonks first met at Mrs Sargent's flat, where Steer brought him one day in 1890 (Joseph Hone, *Life of Henry Tonks*, 1939). Tonks became a lifelong friend of the family and one of Sargent's closest companions, as well as moving in the social milieu of the Hunters and the Hammersleys. In 1910 Tonks accompanied Sargent to Florence on a painting holiday. During the war years he resumed his medical work and exercised his skill as a draughtsman in recording the new techniques of plastic surgery. By 1918 he was engaged as an official war artist, in which capacity he was to travel to Russia in 1919.

Sargent and Tonks left England for the front in late June 1918 and Sargent proceeded via Haig's General Headquarters at Boulogne to General Feilding's Guards Division Headquarters five miles from Berles au Bois. On 16 July he was rejoined by Tonks, and the two shared one of the iron huts which had been built into a high bank to avoid observation, and where the present sketch was executed. General Feilding later recalled: 'He was a delightful companion . . . He used to talk the whole time, and there was always some competition to sit next to him. He took an enormous interest in everything that was going on . . .' (Charteris 1927, p.211). His naïvety as to the conduct of warfare was incredible. Tonks remembered: ' . . . he said to General Feilding one Sunday when the band was playing, "I suppose there is no fighting on Sundays". Sometimes I used to wonder if he knew how dangerous a shell might be . . . he was merely annoyed if they burst sufficiently near to shake him'. 'From Ballymont we went to Arras . . . Here we had two or three weeks together. He did a somewhat elaborate oil painting of the ruined Cathedral' [collection of the Dowager Marchioness of Cholmondeley]' (Charteris 1927, p.212). It was near here that Sargent and Tonks witnessed the event which was to result in Sargent's great war picture, *Gassed* (Imperial War Museum, London).

In this brief impromptu drawing Sargent has managed to evoke the reluctant languidness of the reclining figure, with his hands thrust into his pockets and his back partly propped up against the corrugated-iron wall. At the same time the famous ascetic head is brilliantly defined. In Tonks's obituary in *The Times* a writer, signed G. G–M., spoke of 'a tall pale ascetic type of man with marked Romanesque features' who fussed about after-dinner coffee (Hone, op.cit. p.143). Tonks had a profound respect for Sargent's art and his draughtsmanship in particular. Going through some of the artist's unsold pictures after Sargent's death, he was amazed at the ease of their accomplishment. 'A pencil drawing of a traction engine, put in as rapidly as the pencil would move and apparently quite correct . . . This is one of the qualities of a great artist . . .' Equally Sargent held Tonks's gifts in the highest regard. When he

75 *Henry Tonks*

secured Tonks as a member of the Faculty of Painting at the British School of Rome, Sir Edward Poynter, then Chairman, asked who Professor Tonks was: 'Sargent had difficulty in controlling his indignation and jerked out vehemently, "A great teacher", with a menacing emphasis on the "great".' (Charteris 1927, pp.222–3.)

76 *The Hon Evan Charteris 1921*
(later the Hon Sir Evan Charteris, KC)

Charcoal on paper, 62.2 × 47 (24½ × 18½)

Inscribed, signed and dated (bottom left and right): *to Evan Charteris / John S. Sargent / 1921*

Provenance: By family descent

Literature: Mckibbin 1956, p.89

Lent by the Earl of Wemyss and March, KT

The Hon Evan Charteris was the sixth son of the 10th Earl of Wemyss. He was a distinguished barrister and a Trustee of the National Portrait Gallery and the Tate Gallery. His books included the early biographies of Sargent and of Sir Edmund Gosse. Sargent depicted many members of the Charteris family, including his father, the 10th Earl of Wemyss (1909; private collection).

76 *The Hon Evan Charteris*

77 *Lady Elizabeth Bowes-Lyon*

77 *Lady Elizabeth Bowes-Lyon 1923*

(now Her Majesty Queen Elizabeth the Queen Mother)

Charcoal on paper, 60 × 47 (23½ × 18½)

Inscribed (top left): *Lady Elizabeth Lyon*; signed and dated (bottom left and right): *John S. Sargent 1923*

Literature: Lady Cynthia Asquith, *The Duchess of York* (1928), p.18, repr.; Lady Cynthia Asquith, *The Queen* (1937), p.13, repr.; Mckibbin 1956, p.94

Lent by Her Majesty Queen Elizabeth the Queen Mother

Sargent's drawing of the Queen Mother was made shortly before her marriage to HRH the Duke of York in 1923. There is another drawing, commissioned by Prince Paul of Serbia as a wedding present, in the collection of Her Majesty, and a companion drawing of the Duke of York.

Sargent described the young Duchess as 'The only completely unselfconscious sitter I have ever had' (Asquith, 1937, op. cit.).

78 *Lady Lavery 1923*

Charcoal on paper, 62.2 × 48.3 (24½ × 19)

Inscribed, signed and dated (bottom left and right): *to Lady Lavery | échange amical | John S. Sargent 1923*

Provenance: By family descent

Exhibition: London 1926 (494)

Literature: John Lavery, *The Life of a Painter* (1940), pp.173–4; Mckibbin 1956, p.105

Lent by Mrs Alice Gwynne

Lady Lavery, née Hazel Martyn, was a celebrated beauty and a well-known figure in social circles in London. She was married to the artist Sir John Lavery, with whom Sargent maintained a friendship over many years.

According to Lavery's autobiography, *The Life of a Painter* (op.cit.), this sketch was made after Sargent had visited Lavery's studio while his wife was posing on behalf of the great Russian dancer Anna Pavlova (as the swan from *La Morte du Cygne*), whose portrait he was painting at this time, and whose features Lady Lavery's resembled: 'Sargent came into the studio when Hazel was posing and also remarked on the strange resemblance. He asked her to sit for one of his charcoal drawings, which he did sometime afterwards and was delighted with the result.' Lytton Strachey saw it later and remarked that 'there was always something sinister about Sargent's women. "But", she [Lady Lavery] said, "he has only made me look sixteen!" "That is what is so sinister about you", said Strachey, "and he has caught it".'

79 *Winston Churchill 1925*

Charcoal on paper, 60.3 × 46.4 (23¾ × 18¼)

Signed and dated (bottom left and right): *John S. Sargent 1925*

Provenance: Given to the National Trust

Literature: Mckibbin 1956, p.89

Lent by the National Trust (Chartwell)

Sargent's drawing of Churchill shows the sitter in his robes as Chancellor of the Exchequer. In 1924 Churchill had stood in the General Election as an independent 'Constitutionalist' candidate for Epping, and on the return of Baldwin as Prime Minister, Churchill was offered the Chancellorship. It was seen as a move by Baldwin to absorb as many right-of-centre elements as possible into the Conservative party. Churchill's tenure of office was marked by the return of the gold standard and the difficulties that resulted: deflation, unemployment, the miners' strike and the General Strike. His early Liberalism was seen in the continuation of laissez-faire trading policies and a cautious expansion of the social services.

Sargent and Churchill had several mutual friends, including Sir John and Lady Lavery (see no.78). The exact circumstances of this commission, executed during the last year of Sargent's life, remain unclear.

78 *Lady Lavery*

79 *Winston Churchill*

Fig.21 Painting *Reading* (no.95), with Emily
Sargent watching, Simplon Pass, Switzerland,
1911

Fig.22 Polly Barnard and Rose-Marie posing
for *Reading* (no.95), Simplon Pass, 1911

Figures in a Landscape

During the 1890s Sargent's energies were absorbed in portraiture and mural painting. He certainly travelled, and a handful of works in oil and water-colour prove that he did not shut his eyes or his paint-box. But it is only after 1900 that he consciously turned back to landscape painting, and, as his interest in formal portraiture dwindled, so he gave more of his time and enthusiasm to it. Every summer he would depart for the Continent, accompanied by his sister Emily, sketching companions like the De Glehns and the Stokeses, his other sister Violet and her children, and old family friends. He would go first to the Alps, to Purtud in the Val d'Aosta, or the Simplon Pass, to avoid the heat, descending into the plains of Italy or Spain in the autumn. He was often away for three or four months, sketching compulsively, and bringing back with him quantities of studies in oil and water-colour. He exhibited and sold a few, gave many away, but the residue were littered haphazardly around his studio, or stuffed into drawers.

The theme of the present exhibition has restricted the type of study which could be included. But it has been possible to illustrate in depth certain themes which particularly attracted him, for example the convalescent soldiers painted on his trip to northern Spain in 1903, the figures in Turkish costume painted at Purtud in 1907, the series of girls in Cashmere shawls painted from c.1908 to 1910, and a later group of models in flowing white dresses and parasols painted at the Simplon and at Abriès from 1911 to 1912. In fact his Alpine figure studies fall into distinct periods and styles to a much greater extent than has been realized. Sargent would explore a particular subject in a whole range of studies, and it is fascinating to see his approach in the different media of oil and water-colour. Though always painted on the spot in a vivid impressionist style, his studies of figures are nevertheless carefully composed, and they exude a conscious mood of exotic indolence. A definite decorative idea lay behind each group of pictures and fired Sargent's imagination.

Fig.23 Rose-Marie by the brook at Purtud, 1907, in the same dress as she wears in *The Brook* (no.88)

Fig.24 Painting *Reading* (no.95), Simplon Pass, 1911

80 *Group of Spanish Convalescent Soldiers*

80 *Group of Spanish Convalescent Soldiers* c.*1903*

Water-colour and gouache on paper, 29.8×40.6 (11¾×16)

Inscribed and signed (bottom right): *to my friend Rathbone, John S. Sargent*

Provenance: William G. Rathbone; his daughter, Lady Richmond; thence by family descent

Exhibitions: Probably Royal Society of Painters in Water-Colour, London, 1924 (116); London 1926 (160), repr. 'Souvenir', p.69; Birmingham 1964 (57)

Literature: Ormond 1970, p.250, plate 83

Lent from the collection of the late Lady Richmond

In 1902 and 1903 Sargent was on holiday in Spain. His exact movements in 1902 are not clear, but he wrote to Mrs Gardner from Madrid on 16 June 1903 that he was leaving for Portugal 'and out of the way places' (Isabella Stewart Gardner Museum archives, Boston). On 8 August he wrote from Santiago de Compostela saying that he was travelling on from La Coruna to Venice without returning to Madrid.

There are a small number of related water-colours showing convalescent soldiers in an architectural setting. The location of these was identified by Mckibbin as the Renaissance Hospital Real at Compostela which had been modernized in the 1880s. There is a similar group entitled *Spanish Soldiers* in the Brooklyn Museum, and a courtyard view with a fountain, *Hospital, Santiago* (sold Parke Bernet, 1962). These scenes should not be confused with other Spanish architectural scenes connected with the Alhambra and Charles V's palace at Granada which belong to Sargent's visit of 1912 (see no.98).

81 *A Spanish Convalescent* c.*1903*

Water-colour and pencil on paper, 45.7×30.5 (18×12)

Inscribed and signed (bottom right): *to Mr Wertheimer / John S. Sargent*

Provenance: By descent from Asher Wertheimer

Exhibition: Probably Claridge Gallery, London, 1925 (13)

Literature: Ormond 1970, p.250

Lent anonymously

This sketch almost certainly belongs to the group of Spanish soldiers and convalescents associated with Sargent's visit to Santiago de Compostela in 1903 (see no.80). The brilliantly-defined features of the face contrast with the sketchy clothes and backdrop, while the warm colours and the sad expression of the subject create a most striking effect.

82 *A Spanish Interior* c.*1903*

Colour plate XIII, facing page 80

Water-colour on paper, 57.8×46 (22×18⅛)

Inscribed and signed (bottom right): *to Mr Wertheimer / John S. Sargent*

Provenance: By descent from Asher Wertheimer

Exhibitions: Carfax Gallery, London, 1905 (16); Claridge Gallery, London, 1925 (11)

Lent anonymously

The interior of a Spanish wineshop, presumably painted on Sargent's 1903 trip to Spain. Though the bulk of Sargent's water-colours are of sunlit outdoor scenes, he did paint some marvellously atmospheric interiors of which this is an outstanding example. The treatment of filtered light, as it falls on vivid half-suggested objects and dark recesses, is a *tour de force*. The figures themselves are intensely alive, the young boy intently pouring wine, the splendidly characterful old man, rendered in a few swift strokes, and his young companion propping up the bar. A similar water-colour of a tavern scene in Italy, entitled *Venetian Interior*, is in the Johnson collection, Philadelphia.

Asher Wertheimer was Sargent's most important patron, commissioning the great series of family portraits now in the Tate Gallery. He also owned one of the finest collections of Sargent's water-colours, many of them presented as gifts and evidently chosen for their quality.

83 *Sketching on the Giudecca, Venice* c.*1904*

Water-colour and gouache on paper, 35.5×52.7 (14×20¾)

Provenance: William G. Rathbone; his daughter, Lady Richmond; thence by family descent

81 *A Spanish Convalescent*

82 *A Spanish Interior*

Exhibitions: Paris 1923 (72); Tate Gallery 1926, cat. p.9; Birmingham 1964 (60); *American Artists in Europe 1800–1900*, Walker Art Gallery, Liverpool, 1976–7 (53); *Queen of Marble and Mud: the Anglo-American Vision of Venice*, Nottingham University Art Gallery, 1978 (33)

Literature: *Studio*, xc (15 April 1925), repr. p.82; Mckibbin 1956, p.98 (dated 1904); Ormond 1970, p.255, plate 106

Lent from the collection of the late Lady Richmond

Sargent's Venetian water-colours out-number every other group. Autumn after autumn he returned to the city to sketch its architecture and canals, capturing its ir-ridescent effects of light in some of his most beautiful and colourful water-colours. He usually sketched from a gondola, whose prow, as here, frequently appears in the foreground of his Venetian scenes. The subject of this water-colour is another artist, over whose shoulder we appear to peep, and who in turn sketches the scene before him. It is the foreground detail on which Sargent seizes with such aplomb, and by means of which he makes the scene so vivid. The front of his own boat, cut off and seen head on, leads the eye in. Immediately athwart is the second gondola, its diagonal line dramatically emphasized by the two ropes sweeping across the foreground space. Beyond is a mere suggestive blur of water, rigging and a line of buildings. But the essential forms are there and the enveloping sense of light and atmosphere.

The two figures are Wilfrid and Jane de Glehn, who often accompanied Sargent on his sketching holidays in Europe, and who often feature in his informal oils and water-colours (see no.99). Wilfrid, of German origin, painted portraits and landscapes very much in the manner of Sargent, while his wife, a connection of Henry James, is best known for her portrait drawings. This water-colour was probably done on the same visit to Venice as a water-colour of Jane in a gondola, dated September 1904 (private collection).

83 *Sketching on the Giudecca, Venice*

84 *The Siesta*

84 *The Siesta* c.*1904–8*

Water-colour and gouache on paper, 35.3 × 50.2 (13⅞ × 19¼)
Signed (bottom right): *John S. Sargent*
Provenance: The artist's sister, Emily

Colour plate XV *Miss Eden 1905* (no.86)

Colour plate XVI *The Brook 1907* (no.88)

Sargent; by descent to her niece, Reine Pitman; bequeathed by her to the present owner, the grandson of 'Ginx' Harrison

Exhibitions: Paris, 1923, in aid of the French Red Cross; Claridge Gallery, London, 1925 (161); London 1926 (70), repr. 'Souvenir', p.44; Tate Gallery 1926, cat. p.11; Birmingham 1964 (70)

Literature: M. Hardie, *Famous Water-Colour Painters: VII J. S. Sargent, R.A., R.W.S.* (The Studio, 1930), p.6, plate 3; Mckibbin 1956, p.100 (dated 'Breuil 1908')

Lent by Ben Harrison

A water-colour showing Sargent's close friends and sketching companions, Lawrence ('Peter') Harrison (1866–1937) on the left, and his brother Leonard ('Ginx') Harrison (1870–c.1939) on the right, and perhaps Polly Barnard (see no.89) between them. It is closely related in style and arrangement to an oil of four figures, again including the Harrison brothers, wittily posed on a bank (Fraad collection, New York). This is described by one of the people represented, Lilian Mellor, later Mrs Hare, who recorded her memories of the occasion in a short note, 'Some Memories of a Holiday in Switzerland' (communicated to one of the compilers by Mrs Trench, organizer of the 1962 Falmouth exhibition): 'Our party at G[iomein] was Mr and Mrs Peter Harrison ... Leonard Harrison, Dos Palmer, Sargent and myself. Sargent was always cheerful and very nice to Dos and me. He was doing water-colours. I remember his doing a great bunch of gentians ... He did a sketch of Mrs Peter Harrison one day sitting in the shade under some trees ... He also did an oil sketch of me in the centre, with Leonard Harrison's head on my lap and Peter and Dos in it too. It was in the Academy next summer.'

The painting was not, in fact, exhibited at the Academy, and its dating remains problematical. Mrs Hare remembered the holiday as taking place in 1905, which is just feasible, although Sargent left for Palestine in the autumn. Violet Ormond in a letter to David Mckibbin mentioned a holiday which Sargent had spent at Giomein, a small village above Breuil on the Italian side of the Matterhorn, during which he had painted a local priest, *Padre Sebastiano*. This picture, now in the Metropolitan Museum of Art, New York, was shown in the 1906 summer exhibition of the New Gallery, and would tend to support the

85 *A Siesta*

dating of the Fraad picture to 1905 or perhaps earlier; a picture called *A Siesta* was included in Sargent's one-man show at the Carfax Gallery in 1903.

If the water-colour shown here was painted at the same period as the Fraad oil, then it, too, must have been painted around 1905, and the female figure is presumably Dos Palmer, Peter Harrison's mistress, or Mrs Hare. However, the features of the girl are very much like those of Polly Barnard, who is not known to have been at Giomein. The water-colour has traditionally been dated 1908, when the Barnards and Harrisons were at Purtud; this date is given in Emily Sargent's annotated London 1926 catalogue. It seems unlikely on the other hand that Sargent would have returned to a similar figurative motif after an interval of two or three years, and the identification of Polly Barnard may, therefore, be mistaken. A second water-colour, showing the same trio lying on the ground but somewhat differently arranged, belongs to the Harrison family (repr. London 1926 'Souvenir', p.73); it is inscribed 'to the Comaniacs', a humorous nickname for the friends of Comyns Carr. Both water-colours capture the witty and light-hearted camaraderie that existed between this tight-knit group of

friends, and shows how cleverly Sargent was able to make a satisfying picture from a chance and informal grouping of figures.

85 *A Siesta* c.1907–8 (?)

Colour plate XIV, facing page 81

Water-colour on paper, 40.6 × 53.3 (16 × 21)

Signed (bottom right): *John S. Sargent*

Provenance: H. W. Henderson, thence by family descent

Exhibition: London 1926 (155), repr. 'Souvenir', p.11

Literature: Mckibbin 1956, p.113

Lent anonymously

Traditionally identified as the artist's sister, Violet Ormond, under a parasol, with one of her daughters, probably Reine. Both ladies are asleep, their hats beside them. This water-colour was almost certainly painted on one of the visits to Purtud, and is similar in motif to the water-colour of the same title also shown here (no.84). The figures in the Siesta series are more naturally posed than the later Simplon and Abrès groups (nos.95 to 97).

86 *Miss Eden 1905*

Colour plate xv, facing page 96

Water-colour, gouache and pencil on paper, 50.8 × 35.5 (14 × 20)

Signed and dated (bottom left and right): *John S. Sargent 1905*

Provenance: Sir William Eden; Gooden & Fox; H. W. Henderson and thence by descent

Exhibitions: Royal Society of Painters in Water-Colour, London, 1906 (128); Grosvenor Gallery, London, November 1917 (143); London 1926 (428)

Literature: Mckibbin 1956, p.129

Lent anonymously

Elfrida Marjorie Eden was the daughter of Sargent's friend Sir William Eden, a wealthy amateur artist. She was considered a great beauty, and married Lord Brooke in 1909. In 1924 she became Countess of Warwick when her husband succeeded to the earldom, and she was three times mayor of Warwick. Sargent made a drawing of her in 1909 (formerly Warwick Castle).

Water-colour portraits *per se* are extremely rare among Sargent's output. In this case he has treated the subject as though for an oil portrait, for she is in a characteristic pose in a studio. Sargent's ability to capture a likeness in this medium is almost as complete as in oils: the head is modelled with extreme subtlety and there is an immense enjoyment of the effects of light as the reflections of the red curtain are cast over the sitter's dress.

87 *Shoeing the Ox c.1906–10*

Oil on canvas, 55.9 × 71.1 (22 × 28)

Signed (top left): *John S. Sargent*

Provenance: Lord Rothermere; purchased for Aberdeen Art Gallery by the Macdonald Bequest, 1920

Exhibitions: *Coming of Age*, Bradford, 1925 (87); London 1926 (370), repr. 'Souvenir', p.41

Literature: *Studio*, LXXXII (1921), p.250, repr. p.244; Charteris 1927, p.290; Aberdeen Art Gallery, *Permanent Collection Catalogue* (1968), p.15; Mount 1969, p.472 (105)

Lent by Aberdeen Art Gallery and Museums

This was probably painted in Siena, either

86 *Miss Eden*

in 1906 or 1910, while Sargent was on holiday in Italy. There are a number of studies of oxen in private collections and in the Fogg Art Museum, Cambridge, Massachusetts.

It is very rare to find a subject picture or sketch with quite the same complexity of composition as this among Sargent's oeuvre. It has some of the spontaneity of Sargent's water-colours. The paint is heavily impasted and has suffered as a result.

88 *The Brook 1907*

Colour plate xvi, facing page 97

Oil on canvas, 53.3 × 70 (21 × 27½)

Inscribed and signed (bottom left): *To Violet / John S. Sargent*

Provenance: The artist's sister, Violet Ormond; thence by family descent

Exhibitions: New English Art Club, winter 1907 (86); London 1926 (275), repr. 'Souvenir', p.4; Falmouth 1962 (5); Washington 1964 (88)

Literature: *Art Journal* (1908), p.29; *Athenaeum*, no.4176 (9 November 1907), p.589; *The Times* (4 November 1907), p.10; Downes 1925, p.356; Charteris 1927, p.289 (dated 1909); Mckibbin 1956, p.114 (dated 1912); Mount 1969, p.473 (K123) (dated 1912); Ormond 1970, p.255 (under

note to plate 104), fig. 34

Lent by the Ormond Family

Painted beside the brook at Purtud above Courmayeur in the Val d'Aosta, where Sargent spent a succession of summer holidays from 1904 to 1908. The models were his two nieces, Reine on the left and Rose-Marie on the right, and both are dressed in Turkish costume. Reine is shown in a loose green wrap and cap, while Rose-Marie wears a blue under-dress with a sash at the waist, a white silk patterned over-dress in the form of a long coat, a cap, a necklace of beads and Turkish slippers. A series of four photographs of Rose-Marie in this costume beside the brook at Purtud, one of which is reproduced here, are in the collection of the Ormond family. Although she looks much more mature in the painting, Rose-Marie was in fact only fourteen at this date, and Reine ten. *The Brook* is one of a series of paintings and water-colours of figures in Turkish costume which Sargent painted at Purtud. According to Charteris he took out a trunkload of Turkish clothes from London, and also a stuffed gazelle, the latter almost certainly the model for the three deer which appear in the strange picture of *The Hermit* (Metropolitan Museum of Art, New York). The idea of a series of oriental figure subjects was thus evidently in his mind long before he joined his family and friends at Purtud, and was not the result of a momentary inspiration. One can only speculate on the reasons for his painting these oriental 'fancy' pictures, but it is significant that in his portraiture of this date he was turning to more exotic themes, posing his sitters in Cashmere shawls, and, in one notable work, in a Persian costume with a lute (*Almina Wertheimer*, 1908; Tate Gallery, London).

The figure pictures which Sargent painted at Purtud mark a return to the impressionist themes he had abandoned in the late 1880s, but the style is quite different. In place of the delicate, translucent brushstrokes of his earlier work, the paint in these later pictures is heavily impasted and worked with extraordinary richness. And the models themselves are more artfully posed, with picturesque costumes and accessories that suggest a mood of mystery and enchantment. The girls in *The Brook* conjure up a world of oriental indolence and luxury, the romantic theme of the harem transposed to the vivid setting of an Alpine stream. The idea of the *fête champêtre* is there also, and the painting itself has an almost rococo extravagance of curve and movement. But Sargent's models fuse with their surroundings to a much greater extent than in comparable eighteenth-century paintings. Landscape and figures, subject to the same conditions of light, are treated in a unifying impressionist style. The stream which fascinated Sargent, and which he painted again and again, with and without figures, was of no less interest to him than his models (see figs.6 and 23).

Among other works which Sargent painted at Purtud are two oils of figures in Turkish dresses, trousers and yashmaks, playing chess, *Dolce Far Niente* (Brooklyn Museum), and the *Chess Game* (Harvard University Club, New York), and a number of water-colours (see no.89). A picture of Rose-Marie in a more conventional dress, sitting beside the same stream, called *The Black Brook* (Tate Gallery, London), is very similar in composition. It has usually been dated c.1908, as it was exhibited the following year, but it may also belong to 1907. Previous authorities have overlooked the New English Art Club exhibition and dated *The Brook* variously to 1909 and 1912. The date is, however, confirmed in Emily Sargent's annotated London 1926 catalogue, and Ormond family photographs show that that they were at Purtud in 1907. Reviews of the picture at the NEAC were mixed. The *Athenaeum* critic compared the picture with one by Wilfrid de Glehn of the same title, evidently painted at the same time: 'for the palettes are identical, and Mr Sargent seems to have been infected by his companion's frequent practice of painting the head with exaggerated smoothness in the centre of his composition'. The picture by De Glehn is apparently the one now in the possession of his niece, Mrs Tebbitt. *The Times* described Sargent's *The Brook* as 'two girls lying by the side of a tumbling river. Masterly, of course, and the faces charming; but the hand (which a touch could alter) seems to have been painted so that those who have denounced the hands in every Sargent picture might find themselves justified'.

89 *A Turkish Woman by a Stream* c.*1907*

Water-colour and gouache on paper, 36 × 51 (14⅛ × 20)

87 *Shoeing the Ox*

88 *The Brook*

Inscribed and signed (bottom left): *to Alice Barnard / from her friend John S. Sargent*

Provenance: Mrs Barnard; bequeathed to the Victoria and Albert Museum by her daughter, Dorothy Barnard, 1949

Exhibitions: London 1926 (145); Tate Gallery 1926, cat. p.3

Literature: *Victoria and Albert Museum, Department of Prints and Drawings and Department of Paintings, Accessions 1949* (1961), p.136; Mckibbin 1956, p.83 (dated c.1909)

Lent by the Victoria and Albert Museum

A picture of Polly Barnard (1874–1946) in Turkish costume beside the brook at Purtud in the Val d'Aosta. Polly and Dorothy (see no.29), the daughters of the artist Frederick Barnard, had posed for the little girls in *Carnation, Lily, Lily, Rose* (1885–6; Tate Gallery, London). In the 1900s they and their widowed mother often accompanied the Sargents and Ormonds on their summer holidays in the Alps, and the girls, especially Polly, feature in a number of the pictures which Sargent painted there (see no.95). Another water-colour of Polly in the same dress as that worn by Rose-Marie in *The Brook* (no.88), and in an almost identical pose to the water-colour shown here, is in the Brooklyn Museum, entitled 'Zuleika'. Sargent used his nieces and their friends for a whole succession of oriental pictures painted beside the brook at Purtud. It is fascinating to see his approach to the same subject in the different medium of oil and water-colour. Compared with the heavily impasted surfaces of *The Brook*, the water-colour of Polly Barnard is fluid and transparent, achieving its effect with a minimum of elaboration. The exotic motif and luxuriant setting are, however, very similar in both works.

90 *Cashmere* c.*1908*

Oil on canvas, 70 × 108 (27½ × 42½)

Signed (top right): *John S. Sargent*

Provenance: Purchased by Robert Benson, after the 1909 R.A.; by family descent to his grandson

Exhibitions: R.A., 1909 (496); Tate 1926, cat. p.3; London 1926 (92), repr. 'Souvenir', p.5; Birmingham 1964 (45)

Literature: *Athenaeum*, no.4253 (1 May

89 *A Turkish Woman by a Stream*

1909), p.535; *Guardian* (19 May 1909), p.794; *Spectator*, CII (8 May 1909), p.740; *The Times* (4 May 1909), p.14; Downes 1925, pp.231–2; Charteris 1927, pp.170, 210, 289; M. Birnbaum, *John Singer Sargent* (New York, 1941), p.41; Mckibbin 1956, p.114; Mount 1969, p.473 (ко812); Ormond 1970, pp.76, 255, plate 105

Lent anonymously
Exhibited Leeds and London only

Painted at Purtud on two separate canvases, and then joined together. The model for the figures was the artist's youngest niece, Reine Ormond (later Mrs Hugo Pitman), and not, as previously thought, Rose-Marie. Evidence from contemporary photographs is conclusive (Reine's face is thinner and more delicate than Rose-Marie's), and the new identification was confirmed by Reine herself shortly before her death in 1971. The picture is the largest and most elaborate of Sargent's Alpine figure subjects, and it may well have been worked on in his London studio after his return from the Continent. In contrast to the other Alpine paintings, the landscape is treated summarily, as a backcloth and not as a sharply observed feature in its own right. This is done to emphasise the frieze-like arrangement of the figures, and their statuesque poses. The effect is studied, monumental, mysterious.

91 *The Cashmere Shawl*

90 *Cashmere*

Who are these girls? Where are they going? Why do they gaze out so soulfully? Hooded female figures had haunted Sargent's imagination since the early *Fumée d'Ambre Gris* (Williamstown), suggesting there that the figure is both priestess and *femme fatale*. One should perhaps not read too many symbolic allusions into *Cashmere*. Conceiving the picture as an exhibition piece, the artist wished to give it more formal weight and significance than his purely impressionist figure studies.

The Cashmere shawl, from which the picture takes its title, was a source of fascination to Sargent at this time. The elegant folds of the shawl when draped on the figure, and its subtle textures, appealed to his imagination as a pictorial motif. It is significant that the shawl makes its appearance in several portraits of this period, which are marked by neo-classical influence.

There are also numerous informal oil sketches and water-colours of Sargent's nieces and friends posed in Cashmere shawls (see no.91). *Cashmere* was well received at the Royal Academy of 1909. Critics paid most attention to Sargent's design for the Boston Library murals, *Israel and the Law*, but *Cashmere* came in for its share of praise. *The Times* called it 'exquisite in design, movement and colour', while the *Athenaeum* reviewer wrote that the figures 'are united into the semblance of a picture with extreme cleverness'. Sargent used to give disparaging titles to his pictures, and according to Birnbaum named *Cashmere*, 'The Idiots of the Mountain'. A cartoon parody of the picture by Max Beerbohm, entitled 'Cashmere – and again the queue!', was reproduced in his *Fifty Caricatures* (1913).

91 *The Cashmere Shawl* c.*1908–10*

Water-colour on paper, 50 × 30 (19¾ × 11¾)

Provenance: Purchased for the Museum of Fine Arts, Boston, 1912

Exhibitions: Boston 1925 (34); New York 1926 (7); Boston 1956 (60), repr.; Washington 1964 (116)

Literature: *Bulletin: Museum of Fine Arts*, X (1912), pp.18–20; Downes 1925, p.273; *Museum of Fine Arts Catalogue of Water Colors* (1949), p.164

Lent by the Museum of Fine Arts, Boston (Charles Henry Hayden Fund)

A picture of the artist's niece, Rose-Marie Ormond, posed against a landscape, with a suggestion of a building on her left. She is draped in a Cashmere shawl, the motif for a large group of portraits and figure subjects from around 1907 onwards. The pose of the figure here recalls the large processional picture, *Cashmere* (no.90), though in a more fluid and immediate style. The sweeping folds of the shawl accentuate the sinuous movement of the figure as she pauses momentarily to look back. The beautiful carriage of the head, the slender elegance of the body, are admirably conveyed.

92 *Mosquito Nets 1908*

Oil on canvas, 56.5 × 71.8 (22¼ × 28¼)

Provenance: The artist's sister, Violet Ormond; thence by family descent

Exhibition: Birmingham 1964 (44)

Literature: Mckibbin 1956, p.122; Mount 1969, p.473 (κ0811); Ormond 1970, pp.76, 254, plate 101; Richard Shone, *The Century of Change: British painting since 1909* (1977), repr.

Lent by the Ormond Family

The picture represents the artist's sister Emily, on the left, with Eliza Wedgwood, a member of the famous Wedgwood family, whose mother Sargent had painted in 1896. It was executed at the Villa Longa in Valdemosa, Majorca, where the three friends spent a holiday in the autumn of 1908. Eliza Wedgwood accompanied the Sargents on several such autumn holidays, to Venice, Corfu, Lucca and Lake Garda, from 1906 to 1913, and her reminiscences provide a fascinating picture of their life together (letter to Evan Charteris, 21 May 1925; formerly David Mckibbin collection).

The trio arrived in Valdemosa on 26 September 1908, and, after a night at the primitive local inn, found a flat in the Villa Longa through the kind offices of three resident Spanish artists. They stayed there till late November, and were, in Eliza Wedgwood's words, 'ideally happy . . . The pergola hanging with great bunches of grapes yielded its last on the day we left'. They picnicked with the local artists, played duets, painted and read: 'It was there he painted the water-colour of Emily and me which is in the Tate Gallery – and a wonderful picture of blue pigs which scavenge in the magnificent ilex woods. He also painted in oils such an amusing picture of Emily and me – in what John called "Garde Mangers", Emily's invention for keeping out mosquitoes, and sent me at Christmas his sketch of me'.

92 *Mosquito Nets*

Mosquito Nets is one of Sargent's most delightful conversation pieces. It illustrates his ability to translate a momentary impression into a succinct and satisfying design. The sunlight filters into the room and falls on the two women absorbed in their reading. We see them close-up from above, their figures abruptly cut off, in a direct and very intimate way. Though they appear to be sitting side by side on the same piece of furniture, Emily is in fact in an armchair, with a cushion of the same material as the sofa or day-bed on which her friend reclines. The figures are contained by the diagonal lines of the sofa-back and chair, and by the rounded frames of the nets which enclose the composition at the top, rather as the parasols do in the Simplon series (see no.95). The colour scheme is simple and effective, black dresses against red fabrics and a cool white wall behind. *Mosquito Nets* is more naturalistic and less artfully arranged than Sargent's studies of his nieces and their friends posed in Alpine landscapes (see nos.88 and 96), but it explores the same motif of reclining figures.

Another picture of Polly Barnard lying under a mosquito net, and similarly titled,

is in the White House, Washington DC. Emily Sargent and Eliza Wedgwood often feature in Sargent's informal works, as in the water-colour of Emily sketching, exhibited here (no.93), reclining in a gondola under the Rialto bridge (Ormond family), or breakfasting on the loggia (Freer Gallery, Washington). Two water-colours of Eliza Wedgwood, painted in Majorca in 1908, were in the collections of the Countess of Plymouth and Lady Cynthia Asquith.

93 *Miss Sargent Sketching c.1908(?)*

Water-colour and gouache on white cartridge paper, 47.7 × 34.3 (18¾ × 13½)

Provenance: Given by the artist to his sister, Violet Ormond, as a Christmas present; thence by family descent

Exhibitions: London 1926 (144); Falmouth 1962 (40); Birmingham 1964 (73)

Literature: Mckibbin 1956, p.122

Lent by the Ormond Family

Emily, dressed in black, is painting a water-colour in the doorway of a simple Mediterranean house watched by her friend, Eliza Wedgwood. It may have been painted on the same visit to Majorca as *Mosquito Nets* (no.92) – certainly the colour scheme of the two works is very similar. In her annotated London 1926 catalogue Emily dated this work to 1907, when she, Sargent and Eliza Wedgwood spent a holiday in central Italy, but the simple interior seems more likely to be Majorcan. A second more elaborate water-colour of Emily sketching out-of-doors with Miss Wedgwood beside her, which is known to have been painted in Majorca, is in the Tate Gallery. Other water-colours of Emily sketching include *In the Generalife* (Metropolitan Museum of Art, New York), and *Simplon Pass: The Lesson* (Museum of Fine Arts, Boston). There are many Sargent studies of his painting companions at work (see no.83), a subject that lay naturally to hand, and one which captures the spirit of those relaxed sketching holidays he spent with his family and friends in Southern Europe. In this example the sense of activity and self-absorption is conveyed in a vivid shorthand style that ignores all unnecessary detail, even features. Light seems to breathe in this cool interior with its strong contrasts of blacks, whites and reds.

94 *At Torre Galli, Florence: Ladies in a Garden 1910*

Oil on canvas, 71 × 91.5 (28 × 36)

Provenance: Artist's sale, Christie's, 24 and 27 July 1925 (lot 114), bought in, repr. sale catalogue; presented to the Royal Academy by the artist's sisters, Emily Sargent and Violet Ormond, 1936

Literature: Charteris 1927, p.296; Mount 1969, p.475 (K1016); Ormond 1970, p.76

Lent by the Royal Academy of Arts, London

In the autumn of 1910 Sargent was lent the Villa Torre Galli near Florence by his friend the Marchese Farinola. He was joined there by his sister, Emily, her friend Eliza Wedgwood, Sir William Blake Richmond the painter and his wife, and Wilfrid and Jane de Glehn (see no.83). Sargent wrote to Vernon Lee from Torre Galli (Ormond family): 'So many studies have been started here with the Richmonds figuring in corners that I feel tired – however

93 *Miss Sargent Sketching*

94 *At Torre Galli, Florence : Ladies in a Garden*

they are going tomorrow'.

The loggia features in many of the studies which Sargent painted at the villa, including a picture of the Richmonds and De Glehns, *The Loggia* (Mrs C. S. Payson), and a brilliant conversation piece of Jane de Glehn and Eliza Wedgwood, *Breakfast in the Loggia* (Freer Gallery, Washington DC). In comparison with the vivid and spontaneous impressionism of these works, the picture shown here is far more consciously decorative. The loggia forms a proscenium arch, while the figures, dressed in Cashmere shawls, are shown in carefully studied poses, against the receding perspective of a sym-

metrical garden. Nothing is deliberately unreal, but the elements of the scene are arranged to create a particular mood, an image of oriental indolence and luxury in exotic surroundings.

In 1907 Sargent had painted a series of pictures of his nieces and their friends in Turkish dress (nos.88 and 89). A year later he took out Cashmere shawls, which he had already used in a number of portraits, and posed his models in these, most notably for a processional picture entitled *Cashmere* (no.90). The shawl, with its elegant patterns and subtle textures, appealed to his imagination and his sense of design, and it appears in many of his later figure studies.

The figures in this picture all appear to have been modelled by Jane de Glehn.

95 *Reading 1911*

Water-colour on paper, 51 × 36 (20 × 14)

Signed (upper left) : *John S. Sargent*

Provenance: Purchased for the Museum of Fine Arts, Boston, 1912

Exhibitions : Boston 1925 (45) ; New York 1926 (23) ; Boston 1956 (61) ; Washington 1964 (118)

Literature : *Bulletin Museum of Fine Arts*, x

(1912), p.19; Downes 1925, p.273; *Museum of Fine Arts Catalogue of Water Colors* (1949), p.161; Mckibbin 1956, p.114

Lent by the Museum of Fine Arts, Boston (Charles Henry Hayden Fund)

A water-colour of Polly Barnard reading, on the left, and the artist's niece, Rose-Marie, on the right. It is one of a group of oils and water-colours painted by Sargent at the Simplon Pass in Switzerland, in which his nieces and their friends are posed in voluminous white dresses and parasols. Like the earlier series of figures dressed in Turkish costume and Cashmere shawls, the mood is one of exotic indolence and luxury, heightened by the setting of Alpine meadows. The figures are arranged in consciously decorative poses, and there is often, as here, a sense of witty and playful relationship between them.

There are a number of interesting photographs of Sargent at work on this particular water-colour, watched by his sister, Emily, together with a photograph of the two girls in the identical pose (figs.21, 22 and 24).

96 *The Pink Dress 1912*

Oil on canvas, 54.6 × 66 ($21\frac{1}{4}$ × 26)

Provenance: The artist's sister, Violet Ormond; thence by family descent

Exhibitions: London 1926 (1), repr. 'Souvenir', p.43; Falmouth 1962 (3); Washington 1964 (89)

Literature: Downes 1925, p.341; Charteris 1927, p.210; repr. Meynell 1927; Mckibbin 1956, p.114 (dated 1909); Mount 1969, p.475 (K1217) (dated 1912), repr. between pp.144–5; Ormond 1970, p.76

Lent by the Ormond Family

A picture of the artist's niece, Rose-Marie, painted in the French Alps, at Abriès, Dauphiné. The Ormonds spent a summer holiday there with Sargent and other friends in 1912. Stylistically and thematically *The Pink Dress* is closely connected to the figure subjects which Sargent painted at the Simplon. These include an oil of *Two Girls in White Dresses* (Dowager Marchioness of Cholmondeley), and a series of water-colours of single figures or groups of two: *Reading, Simplon Pass: The Tease, Simplon Pass: the Green Parasol* (all three Museum of Fine Arts, Boston); and *Simplon Pass* (formerly Charteris collection). Common to

95 *Reading*

96 *The Pink Dress*

97 *Girl in a Pink Dress Reading*

98 *Blind Musicians*

this group are ballooning white or pink dresses obviously chosen carefully by the artist for their decorative qualities (not what you would ordinarily wear in the Alps), bonnets secured by scarves, and parasols which are often held behind the head as part of an enclosing decorative pattern. The care which Sargent took in posing his models, usually his nieces or their friends, can be seen in the series of photographs of him at work in the Alps (Ormond family), including a series of seven or eight connected specifically with *Reading* (no.95). A water-colour of Rose-Marie in the same or a similar pink dress is also exhibited here (no.97).

The motif of *The Pink Dress* goes back to the early impressionist pictures by Monet and his circle of women in summery dresses decoratively arranged in landscapes. The figure of Rose-Marie is much more simply and classically posed than in Sargent's earlier sequence of oriental subjects (see nos.88 and 89), although the high viewpoint gives a close-up effect and enhances the sense of immediacy. It is typical of Sargent to wish to catch his models from unusual angles. Rose-Marie is shown by the base of a tree, her knees partly raised, sitting perhaps on a slight bank, with the ground falling away to the right. Though painted in

Sargent's boldest manner, with vigorously impasted brush-strokes and a highly-keyed palette, the figure is firmly observed (apart from some lapses with the right wrist and hand), and the head is a charming portrait vignette. The title is perhaps a misnomer, for the colour of the dress, as interpreted in these particular conditions of light, is predominantly bluish and greenish-grey rather than pink. The parasol, balancing the ballooning mass of the dress on the right, is dark blue, and behind is a russet meadow treated in a blurred and sketchy style.

97 *Girl in a Pink Dress Reading* *1912*

Water-colour on paper, 70.5×38 ($27\frac{3}{4} \times 15$)

Provenance: The artist's sister, Violet Ormond; thence by family descent

Exhibitions: Tate Gallery 1926, cat. p.7; Birmingham 1964 (77)

Lent by the Ormond Family

A water-colour of Rose-Marie Ormond, wearing the same or a similar dress as that shown in *The Pink Dress* (no.96). In the 'Sargent Trust List' (Ormond family) the water-colour is said to have been painted at

Abriès in 1912. Another water-colour of Rose-Marie in this dress with a black hat was formerly with Knoedler. Both belong to the group of Alpine figure studies painted at Abriès and the Simplon. The static effect of the figure in this example is relieved by the vivid lines defining the flounces of the skirt and cape.

98 *Blind Musicians* *1912*

Water-colour and pencil on paper, 39.4×53.3 ($15\frac{1}{2} \times 21$)

Signed (upper left): *John S. Sargent*; inscribed on the back (in artist's hand): *The Generalife / John S. Sargent / 31 Tite Street / Chelsea*

Provenance: Artist's sale, Christie's, 24 July 1925 (lot 3); Charles Deering; Sir Charles Murray, Bt, MP; Christie's, 29 April 1927 (lot 21); purchased by Aberdeen Art Gallery, half the auction price being met by Sir Charles Murray

Exhibitions: Probably Royal Water-Colour Society, summer 1913 (23), as 'Blind Beggers'; *Jubilee Fifty Years of British Art*, Cartwright Art Gallery, Bradford, 1954 (161)

Literature: *Aberdeen Art Gallery Catalogue*

(1937), plate lvi; *Aberdeen Art Gallery Permanent Collection Catalogue* (1968), p.87

Lent by Aberdeen Art Gallery and Museums

Sargent returned to Spain in the autumn of 1912 and is recorded at work in Granada and Aranjuez. Of the latter he wrote: 'These Spaniards are the most amiable people in the world, they put themselves out for you in the most extraordinary way. With the common people it is no disadvantage being an American, for the newspapers told them that they gave us the most tremendous licking in Cuba.' (Charteris 1927, p.171.)

On 6 November 1912 Sargent had written from Granada to Mrs Curtis (see no.11) to say that he and Emily were still at work, and finding it hard to leave, although the De Glehns were in the process of doing so (D. Mckibbin collection). On 15 December Ralph Curtis wrote to Mrs Gardner (Isabella Stewart Gardner Museum archives) to tell her that a fortnight before he had seen Sargent's Alhambra work: 'They are mostly in oils, small figure pieces, grape gardens, crumbling Arab courtyards and gipsy caves, grey donkeys etc. There were a few masterly aquarelles as well'. Sargent painted nearly a dozen oils, including *Spanish Gipsies* (R.A., 1913; untraced), *Hospital at Granada* (Melbourne), and a number of studies of courtyards and fountains. Among the water-colours are several figure subjects, including the group of Emily sketching with Mrs de Glehn and Dolores, called *In the Generalife* (Metropolitan Museum of Art, New York), previously dated to 1902 by Mckibbin, and *Granada: Shelling Maize* (Ormond family), where the figures, though sketchier than those in *Blind Musicians*, are posed against white in very much the same style.

One of Sargent's chief characteristics as a water-colourist is the recording of an immediate impression. In this work he has deliberately chosen to truncate the composition to the right and in the foreground while extending the empty area to the left. He has pencilled in the main features of the figures and then rapidly covered the rest of the paper in a limited colour range, mainly using his preferred blues and violets. There is little use of the white of the paper, and Sargent has preferred to emphasize the ferocity of the sunlight in the brightness of the instruments.

99 *The Green Dress*

The suggestion of blindness is brilliantly realized in the intense stare of the figure to the left playing a mandolin and evidently singing in a high key. He is contrasted with the glum expression of the figure on the right, strumming away on his guitar, whose eyes are lost in the shadow of his sombrero. Both figures are reminiscent of the musicians in *El Jaleo* (Isabella Stewart Gardner Museum, Boston), painted thirty years previously. The combination of blindness and music must have been a poignant subject for Sargent. On his second visit to Spain in 1879–80 he had tried to make researches into Spanish folk-songs for his friend Vernon Lee (see no.33), writing to her that 'The best (songs) are what one hears in Andalucia, the half African Melaguemas, dismal, restless chants that it is impossible to note.' (Charteris 1927, p.49.)

99 *The Green Dress* c.*1912* (?)

Water-colour on paper, 43 × 32.5 (17 × 12¾)

Inscribed and signed (top left): *to my friend Premp / John S. Sargent*

Provenance: Wilfrid de Glehn; thence by family descent

Exhibition: London 1926 (125)

Literature: Mckibbin 1956, p.98 (dated 1912)

Lent anonymously

A picture of Jane de Glehn sitting on a Victorian sofa, draped in a Cashmere shawl. The sitter and her husband, Wilfrid (nicknamed Premp), were both artists and friends of Sargent, and they often feature in his work (see nos.83 and 94). The tall and elegant Jane was a favourite model for several outdoor sketches painted in Italy and the Alps. It is not known where or when this water-colour was executed, but it belongs in style to a small group of interior scenes with figures. It is scarcely a portrait, the features barely defined, but it is nevertheless full of atmosphere and character. The sitter is reading a book, her voluminous skirt filling the space in a relaxed composition. Her head is reflected in the mirror behind, and there is a console table on the left. Like *Mosquito Nets* (no.92), the water-colour conveys the leisurely and cultivated mood of Edwardian life.

100 '*Thou Shalt Not Steal*'

101 *The Interior of a Hospital Tent*

100 '*Thou Shalt Not Steal*' *1918*

Water-colour and pencil on paper,
50.8 × 33.6 (20 × 13¼)

Signed, inscribed and dated (bottom left):
John S Sargent Arras 1918

Provenance: Sir Muirhead Bone; presented
by him to the Imperial War Museum, 1919

Exhibitions: Tate Gallery 1926, cat. p.5;
London 1926 (105)

Literature: *Imperial War Museum: Concise
Catalogue of Paintings, Drawings and Sculpture
of the First World War 1914–1918* (second
edition, 1963), p.266; Ormond 1970 p.234,
col. plate XVII

Lent by the Trustees of the Imperial War
Museum

In August 1918 Sargent and Tonks (no.75)
moved on to Arras, which had been devas-
tated. Tonks wrote:'. . . Colonel Hastings
found us quarters in the best uninjured house
in the place. Here we had two or three
weeks together. He did a somewhat elaborate oil painting of the ruined Cathedral
[The Dowager Marchioness of Chol-
mondeley] and a great many water colours of
surprising skill. I never could persuade him
to work in the evening when the ruined
town looked so enchanting; he worked
systematically morning and afternoon'.
(Charteris 1927, p.212.)

A large number of sketches at the
Imperial War Museum, the Fogg Art
Museum and the Metropolitan Museum of
Art, New York, record Sargent's activity
at this time. He was painting a monumental

work for a proposed Hall of Remembrance,
entitled *Gassed* (Imperial War Museum),
based on an event witnessed near Arras.
The lack of emotion in Sargent's war
pictures is partially explained by his own
personality and also by the fact that he
never witnessed any of the more harrowing
episodes in the war. In this picture the
impression of light falling through the
foliage while the soldiers furtively snatch at
the fruit is brilliantly evoked and continues
Sargent's prevailing interests, seen in the
Alpine sketches.

101 *The Interior of a Hospital Tent 1918*

Water-colour on paper, 39.4 × 52.6 ($15\frac{1}{2} \times 20\frac{3}{4}$)

Signed and dated (bottom right): *John S. Sargent 1918*

Provenance: Presented to the Imperial War Museum by the artist, 1919

Exhibition: London 1926 (543)

Literature: M. Hardie, *Famous Water-colour Painters: VII J. S. Sargent, R.A., R.W.S.* (The Studio, 1930), plate vii; *Imperial War Museum: Concise Catalogue of Paintings, Drawings and Sculpture of the First World War 1914–1918* (second edition, 1963), p.266; Mount 1969, p.361

Lent by the Trustees of the Imperial War Museum

Late in September 1918, while gathering material for *Gassed* near Peronne, Sargent was struck down with influenza and taken to a casualty unit near Roisel. Here he was treated by Doctor Stobie of Oxford and spent a week in bed, 'in a hospital bed', he wrote to Mrs Gardner, 'with the accompaniment of wounded, and the chokings and coughings of gassed men, which was a nightmare – it always seems strange on opening one's eyes to see the level cots and the dimly lit long tent looking so calm, when one was dozing in pandemonium'. (Charteris 1927, p.216.)

Sargent's obvious emotional response to the wounded and his proximity to them is not really borne out in his war pictures, least of all here, where the atmosphere is almost that of a convalescent home. Although it lacks some of the vigour and the strong sense of colour of the water-colours of the previous decade, there is a great interest in light and many of his war sketches feature a strong sense of the mass and volume of tarpaulins and tents.

102 *Study of a Nude Model*

Water-colour on paper, 47 × 54.5 ($18\frac{1}{2} \times 21\frac{1}{2}$)

Inscribed and signed (top right): *to my friend Goscombe John / John S. Sargent*

Provenance: Sir Goscombe John, RA, given with his collection to the National Museum of Wales

102 *Study of a Nude Model*

Exhibition: London 1926 (536), 'Figure study'

Literature: Mckibbin 1956, p.111

Lent by the National Museum of Wales, Cardiff

According to Mckibbin, a study of Luigi Mancini, one of a prolific family of Italians whom Sargent employed as models, chiefly for his Boston murals. There is an oil of the same model in a similar pose in the Forbes Magazine Collection. Sargent had drawn extensively from the nude as a student in Paris, and later his murals necessitated a huge number of life drawings. This water-colour is a pleasant contrast, in its unstudied naturalism, to these more consciously posed figures. The model appears to have fallen asleep, with one arm hooked through some drapery, and a rough wooden staircase behind. The structure of the body is firmly given, but the study is more remarkable as an intimate view in the studio alive with light and atmosphere. It is difficult to date at all precisely but must be after 1900 on grounds of style. In 1917 Sargent painted a sequence of water-colour studies of nude Negroes in Florida.

Goscombe John, to whom the study is inscribed, was a distinguished sculptor.

Index